THE MEANING OF THE BODY

THE MEANING
OF THE BODY

BY
JACQUES SARANO

TRANSLATED BY
JAMES H. FARLEY

PHILADELPHIA

THE WESTMINSTER PRESS

PUBLISHED BY THE WESTMINSTER PRESS®

PHILADELPHIA, PENNSYLVANIA

PRINTED IN THE UNITED STATES OF AMERICA

To my friend
Dr. Paul Tournier

CONTENTS

PREFACE

THE SUBJECT DEALT WITH IN THE FOLLOWING PAGES BY DR. Jacques Sarano seems to me to be essential. For several centuries the natural sciences and the moral sciences worked side by side, as in two adjoining houses, but the houses were separated by a party wall with no door of communication.

A profitable work has been done in each of the two houses, above all, perhaps, in the house of science. Thus, to speak only of man, our knowledge has made amazing progress (insofar as man is an object of scientific study). As a living being he is endowed with a body studied by anatomy, with an often injury-impaired body studied by pathology, each cell and organ of which are the seats of functions studied by psychology: the sensory and motor faculties, memory, consciousness, and the innate and conditioned reflexes.

In his collective dimensions he is studied by sociology, cultural geography, and Marxist dialectic.

The progress of our knowledge will undoubtedly continue to accelerate in each of these domains, for each discovery, each more exhaustive analysis opens the way to new research, observations, hypotheses, and experiments.

But considerable progress has also been made in the house next door. Man is differentiated from all other living beings by certain needs, aspirations, sufferings, and convictions that play a decisive role in his personal life. These are experiences which he meets within himself, to which he can testify. He can evoke, describe, assert, and communicate these. Yet they rigorously escape all scientific, objective observation.

Even more, although he is linked with all other men through these qualities of the spirit, he is also distinguished through them. Since Montaigne and, especially, Jean Jacques Rousseau, man appears as a unique being, incomparable to any other, who can never know himself (and yet, who ever really knows himself?) except as full of contradictions and mystery, incommunicable to others and to himself. What counts for him is that which he has lived personally and which he is alone in having lived.

As an object of the natural sciences, he is a prisoner of time and space, for science knows only that which is calculated and measured. As a spiritual being, he breaks loose from time and space. His thought can travel more quickly than any astronaut beyond the confines of the world. It can go back in an instant beyond the most distant geological ages. He carries within him a sense of the beautiful, the true, and the good that defies all attempts at measurement. He questions himself concerning the world and concerning himself. He has need of grasping not only things, but the meaning of things. He does not simply suffer or rejoice, but questions himself concerning the meaning of his suffering or of his rejoicing. He does not simply live and die, but questions himself concerning the meaning of life and death, of his personal life and death. He is able to experience communion with others, to have personal encounter with God.

Man belongs to two worlds, the world of phenomena and the world of values. Science reveals man to himself as strictly determined, and yet he carries within himself a certitude of freedom. He has the conviction of being truly man only through this capacity to choose, to believe, to engage himself personally in his relationships with himself, with the world, with others, and with God, even when he proudly rejects the latter. He knows that he is man because he can always say yes or no, and not say it by chance. Since Kierkegaard, existential philosophy has accented this tragic freedom, this dread of choices, this need for the meaning of things.

Whatever be the progress of the works accomplished in each of our two houses, it is clear that a valid knowledge and a valid conception of man cannot be found separately on one side or the other, not even by an accumulation, by an investigator who would learn in turn all that could be learned in both houses. A synthesis is necessary. It would be necessary to understand how these two worlds to which man belongs are connected, how they are connected within *man himself*.

Some steps have already been taken in each of the two houses in the direction of a synthesis. Thus, on the side of science, the frontier so long separating the body and the soul has drastically been crossed. Psychosomatic medicine has taught us much concerning their mutual influence and interdependence.

On the side of the moral sciences, we have gone far beyond the frontier between the psychical life and the spiritual life. Religious psychology, the psychology of art, cognitive philosophy, have taught us much concerning their mutual influences, to what extent the ensemble of psychic characteristics conditions faith, the sense of guilt, the scale of aesthetic and ethical values, and to what extent the spiritual life modifies the ensemble of psychic characteristics. The discoveries of psychology have profoundly marked art, philosophy, and even theology.

But it is the other frontier, that of the center, that has not been crossed. Our party wall, the junction between the objective world of phenomena and the subjective world of values, remains nearly impenetrable. Dr. Sarano shows this very clearly in this book dealing with the field of medicine. He emphasizes the merits of psychosomatic medicine. Yet it should be understood that psychosomatic medicine has not yet re-

solved the most difficult problem. This problem is that of the
connections between the body and the soul, taken this time
in the spiritual sense of the term (what Aquinas called the
"sharp point of the soul," and what other thinkers call the
spirit).

Whatever be the words employed, everyone admits that the
problem here is an extremely difficult one to resolve. Indeed,
it is possible to give, in scientific language, an objective description of man and of the phenomena that unfold there, and
then to turn around and, in picturesque and colored language
(i.e., in poetic and mythical language), evoke the subjective
experiences of man's spiritual life. This does not yet resolve the
problem. In fact, it barely touches it. This problem has occupied me for many years, and I would say that such an effort
must be achieved through the elaboration of an anthropology,
of a valid, true, and universal conception of man considered in
his unity and in his totality.

Common to the two approaches is experiment: the scientific
experiment of the scholars and the personal experiments lived
by the subject himself; the experiment made on him in examining him as an object and that which he makes spontaneously
and which he can understand only by paying attention to it
himself. I can speak of my life or relate circumstances. I can
say: see what has happened to me, to this one, to that one, and
how each individual has felt that which he has lived. I can
also speak of the case in a scientific fashion, of that which I
have discovered in examining the patient, the illness he suffers
from, and its development. But these two experiments are of
two different orders, subjective and objective, neither reducible
to the other. Yet there must be a link between them, since
they involve the same person.

It is to this quest that the Medicine of the Person is devoted. Some consider it to be a spiritual medicine as opposed
to a physical medicine. In a sense this is true. Dr. Paul Platt-
ner has said of the Medicine of the Person that it reintroduced the world of values into medicine. We dare to say what

everyone can observe, but concerning which an orthodox physician does not permit himself to speak because it seems to him to be a methodological error, namely, that the spiritual and moral life of a patient plays an important role in the development of his physical and psychical life, in his illness and in his healing. But this is not to say that a medicine of the person can ignore the importance of physical and psychical phenomena that bring about the illness. To do so would be to strengthen even more the party wall which should be eliminated. On the contrary, it seeks to understand man as a whole, the man in which the spirit is as inseparable from the body as from the soul, the man whose spirit expresses itself only in his body and in his soul.

From this it is understandable that one of the sessions of the conference on the Medicine of the Person should be entirely devoted to this problem of the meaning of the body for the person. Dr. Sarano was responsible for presenting the principal paper, and other participants were to supplement his effort by treating of the special meaning that the body assumes for various categories of persons: the elderly (Prof. Karl Stoevesandt, of Bremen), the child (Dr. Pierre Robert, of Marseille), the woman (Dr. Max Wallet, of Paris), the critical, pained, surgical patient (Dr. Ernest Irrmann, of Strasbourg), the psychosomatic patient (Dr. Roland Pierloot, of Louvain), the invalid (Miss Suzanne Fouché, of Paris), in married love (Dr. Theo Bovet, of Basel), and finally, the meaning of the body in the Bible (myself).

Dr. Sarano was especially qualified to study, in his basic report, the general question of the meaning of the body for the human person and the perspectives that it opens for our conception of man and of medicine. A specialist in gastroenterology at Valence (Drome), he combines a scientific authority and great medical experience with a good philosophical formation and a living faith. He is already well known through his first books: *La Guérison* (Paris: Presses Universitaires de France, 1955), *La Culpabilité* (Paris: Colin, 1957), *Médecine et médecins* (Paris: Seuil, 1959), and various articles, notably on the meaning of pain.

His report merited being enlarged and put into finished form and published in book form. I am pleased to present the finished product to the cultivated public, for it brings views to this important subject that are penetrating, original, and quite thought-provoking. Indeed, he goes to the heart of the problem: How can the body be at one and the same time an object, the object of scientific research and of that judgment which man can bring on his body as on a thing distinct from himself, and a subject, the person itself, which his body lives, which is identified with him and witnesses to this experiment?

The stakes in this study are considerable and go far beyond the field of medicine: it involves the elaboration of a new doctrine of man in which all our present knowledge of him can be integrated, a doctrine without which true civilization could not be possible. Antiquity had its conception of man, as did both the Middle Ages and the Renaissance. But today, as a natural consequence of the compartmentalization to which I have alluded with the image of our two houses, we no longer have a conception of man. Marxism alone can pretend to have one, possibly because it purports to know nothing of the second house. (Marxism considers this second house as a fiction or an epiphenomenon, without taking into account that its own very existence and its own aspirations have a spiritual meaning and function.)

The problem can also be simplified from the other side, from the idealistic side. We can enclose ourselves so tightly in the second house that the other, the objective reality of which the body rightly reminds us each day, is ignored or despised. The concept of the person requires that the problem not be dodged, but confronted; that neither the objective, phenomenal, and social aspect of man nor his spiritual, subjective, and interpersonal aspect be neglected; and that he be considered neither as an isolated individual nor as a mere fragment of the mass that determines him. Emmanuel Mounier, the founder of

Personalism, has contributed more than anyone else to posing, in his precise terms, this formidable problem.

We study it from our viewpoint as physicians, but the problem is met with again and again in all disciplines. This is why Dr. Sarano's work is well adapted to enlisting the attention not only of physicians and patients, but of philosophers, artists, educators, theologians, and all who grasp the drama of our age.

The work of art also has a body: the stone of the sculptor, the canvas and paints of the painter, the instrument of the musician, the words that the poet must utter to express his feelings.

A country also has a body: its mountains and rivers, its fields of wheat and its factories. The student, at school, also has a body: a heredity, a physiological and mental mechanism with which he must assimilate the knowledge that is taught to him. The church also has a body: the vaults of its cathedrals, its rites, its organization. The law also has a body: its codes, its courts of justice, its jurisprudence, and its police force, without which justice and equity would be only reveries and which, however, can achieve justice and equity only so imperfectly.

One cannot nurse a sick person, manage a factory, lead a country, or do any work whatever, if he sees his task simply as if it were purely technical. But neither can he content himself with puddling unalloyed principles. But how to join the two, how to combine the spirit of geometry and the spirit of Pascal's finesse, if it is not in ourself, since the person is the place of the spirit's incarnation.

This signifies a way of living and acting, open to both the visible and the invisible, to harsh material reality and ineffable spiritual reality. But it also signifies a difficult effort of thought that of necessity takes the form of philosophical thought.

It is possible that some readers, quite absorbed with human problems but little accustomed to philosophical language, will sometimes have difficulty following Dr. Sarano in certain of his

pages that they will find too abstract. I want them not to become discouraged. I want them really to try to understand what
they do not yet understand, to grasp the importance and the
scope of this problem of the body. It serves nothing to com-
plain about the dehumanization of modern medicine and the
modern world if one is not disposed to make a small effort of
thought in order to elaborate a new conception of man capable of renewing medicine and the world.

Why, then, has God not created us pure spirits, angels, outside of time and space? Why has he created us as corporeal
beings, dependent upon this so burdensome and limited body,
which unceasingly checks the momentum of our spirits? Why
are we created dependent upon a frail body susceptible to falling ill and dying? This must have a meaning, not that of a
shackle but of a truth that it is necessary to understand, to
learn, and to live.

Every idea of creation, moreover, implies an idea of materiality. Before man, God created light, the stars, atoms, elec-
trons, all the body of the world. If there were not this body of
the world, we would not question the meaning of the world.
What meaning would the world have if it did not exist as material reality? If physicians have too much neglected the importance of the spiritual life of their patients and the enormous
role that it plays in their health, the philosophers and theologians, for their part, have too much neglected the importance
of the body. A double movement is therefore necessary, a reciprocal discovery, a dialogue, a breach in the party wall.

All the churches speak of incarnation, but they generally
suggest a contempt of the body, as if the spirit had debased itself instead of fulfilled itself in this wonderful venture that God
has willed. We find in all our patients, especially in our pious
patients, a certain contempt for the body, even when they surround it with hypochondriacal solicitude. Their failures, their
limitations, their temptations, their faults, their sufferings —
the responsibility for all this is shifted onto the body, this ac-
cursed, obstinate, exacting body without which one could fi-

nally achieve the dreamed of plenitude. But without this body, could one achieve anything at all?

I do not believe that any man completely accepts his body. And the revolt against the body is a kind of civil war that exhausts the forces of life. A complete harmony with one's self implies necessarily a harmony with one's body, this maligned, maltreated, underrated pauper, which so often takes its tragic revenge in illness, thus reminding us bluntly of its resolute reality.

Moreover, one cannot accept life and accept the world without accepting one's body. It is through my body that " I am in the world," and it is also through my body that " I mark myself off from the world." Dr. Sarano reminds us of this with insistence. A medicine of the person which would ignore the body would be nothing more than a medicine of reverie. Instead of rebelling against the body, is it not more correct and more fruitful for us to listen to the lesson it teaches, which we have so much difficulty understanding?

This lesson of life is not only a scientific lesson, but also a spiritual lesson. I would even say a revelation. Here, we are at the heart of the problem. It is commonly imagined that the body belongs to the material world and the soul to the spiritual world; that between our two adjoining houses the body can be left to the first, that of scientific investigation, whereas in the second house one is concerned only with spiritual things; that in the first, one will learn anatomy, physiology, and psychology, whereas in the second, one will learn philosophy, art, and theology.

Dr. Sarano boldly proclaims the absurdity and the danger of such a prejudice: it is the body itself that has a spiritual meaning, and one cannot comprehend anything either of the spirit or of the person if one cuts them off from the body. The author goes so far as to speak of the body as a " sacrament," that is, as a sign from God.

With such a thesis, so contrary to our modern thinking, Dr. Sarano is clearly going to expose himself to lively reproaches from both sides, from experts in scientific matters as well as from those who are specialists in questions of faith. He will be told that it is mixing and confusing what should be absolutely differentiated, that he is committing a serious methodological error, that his attitude is no longer either strictly medical or strictly spiritual. For, in the eyes of those who labor in each of the two houses, the sin par excellence is to break through the party wall, to go beyond the strict limits that have been set for each discipline.

Many people feel that our modern thought suffers from this scission between our intellectual disciplines. Many have an idea that the meaning of the human, the meaning of the person, cannot be rediscovered without looking at it from both sides at once. But as soon as one endeavors to exercise, as physician, a spiritual ministry among the sick, as soon as spiritual concepts are taken into account in a scientific work, there are some people in both camps who protest. Not only are there scientists who say that this is no longer science and physicians who say that it is no longer medicine, but there are philosophers and theologians who fear that such thought leads only to confusion.

I think that the people on both sides are obeying a conservative instinct in this matter. For, in both houses, the invasion through the party wall of a group speaking another language and obeying other methods brings distressing upheaval. One can no longer work tranquilly in the interior, according to the comfortable norms that explicitly define the particular field of research. After centuries of war, an armistice had been concluded between the natural sciences and the moral sciences. A well-guarded line of demarcation had been fixed, assuring peace in each camp.

The philosophers and theologians were left to debate abstract ideas leisurely in their corner and the faithful were left to worship in their chapels, provided that they not leave their given area and that they not aspire to return to reality, to this body, which is society, politics, the school, science, and economics, where their revelations are irrelevant. One would deferentially tip his hat to them from a distance, but without having to take account of their way of looking at things. After such amenities of politeness were performed, a very fruitful work could be pursued, constructing the coherent edifice of science, resolving all problems from a purely objective and technical point of view.

But in this way, one has lost *man!* Many thinkers are giving an account of this today. There is no longer a soulless body in one chapel and a bodiless soul in the other. Also, there are men on both sides who feel that although it is first necessary to separate the problems in order to study them, it is also necessary, as a next step, to bring them into confrontation, to enter into dialogue, to cross the demarcation line.

If we want to recover the meaning of man and of the human, to build a personalist civilization, we must have the courage, as does Dr. Sarano, to break through the party wall. We must brave the critics that a book such as this can raise. We must dare to leave the frequented and protected paths in order to elaborate a bolder, freer, truer, and more synthetical thought.

We are only at the beginning. The effort of comprehension and of dialectic between the separate disciplines has been neglected for so long that such a work is today still very strange and very laborious. We cannot even understand the same word in the same way in all the faculties of the same university. Think, for instance, of the contempt for philosophy shown by most physicians, for whom it is merely literature and dreams without practical import for their therapeutic activity. Much time and work will still be necessary before we can formulate a valid and universal conception of man. A book such as this one seems to me an initial step on this difficult and necessary route.

DR. PAUL TOURNIER

Geneva, August 3, 1962

INTRODUCTION

Critique of a Global Method [1]

I

It is well known how Paul Tournier, in the spirit of the Medicine of the Person that he has defined, practiced, and propagated for more than twenty years through his books, lectures, and personal contacts, has been able to gather about him physicians from numerous countries. They have bound themselves together, through work and friendship, to establish a common practice and doctrine. It is now, in fact, a community, but one freely open to new constituents (of which I am one), physicians or not, believers and unbelievers, within an inspiration that is nevertheless Christian. I would even say that this inspiration, although it avoids being exclusive, is basic to the community. This is of the greatest importance to understand when I state that I will deal with objectives and methods.

Moreover, this account introduces a study that, hopefully, will contribute to the formulation of an anthropology (in the broad sense), to a doctrine. Without such a doctrine, the inspiration and the practice are in danger of lacking substance and soon being lost in smoke. The difficulty will be in trying not to smother the inspiration under the explication, while at the same time building up the former by means of the latter.

It is difficult to define this inspiration, this work of Tournier, in a few summary words. It involves the perception of an essential defect in the objective medicine of the technician, such as we ordinarily practice today, and the need for a clinical and therapeutic comprehension of the whole person (we say, indeed, *whole*, that is, at one and the same time organic, psychical, social, cultural, and spiritual).

It has become commonplace to denounce this defect in objective medicine. It is no longer possible to count the publications that, under psychosomatic and other rubrics, attempt to restore (without repudiating any of the most modern scientific attainments) a medicine that regards the problems of man in his history and in the environment in which he lives.

But Paul Tournier, in a single effort that responds precisely to that call of which I spoke, a call that does not conceal but clearly states its religious source, has immediately and decisively gone beyond all other similar attempts. He follows their "logic" to its end, laying bare both the fruitfulness and the risks, the richness and the imprudence, of such an orientation.

Tournier has frequently replied to the objections raised and that will continue to be raised for a long time to come against his *Medicine of the Person.*

It is his position that if it is admitted that the ensemble of psychic characteristics, the "moral faculties," the environment, the problems of life, trust and mistrust, frustrations, the general attitude of man, faith and the absence of faith, all play together a principal role in the etiology and the therapy of organic and especially of "functional" diseases (the former often through the latter), then medicine must not be afraid of extending as far and as deeply as possible its therapeutic action. And medicine must do this not only through the analysis and elucidation of life's problems, but also by bringing the patient to a realization of his stifled, ignored, repressed, or rejected spiritual (and perhaps religious) resources. It is the fervent Christian who speaks in Tournier, who attempts to practice his medicine as a complete medicine. That is, he is certain of his total responsibilities and possibilities in every do-

main, even and above all in the spiritual. He is no less certain
of the total responsibilities of his patients, if it is true that nothing should be neglected when it is a question of healing, of
recovering the balance and the fullness of life, that is, health.

II

Is this not to mix up the cards, to mistake the physician for
the confessor? Tournier has been sharply rebuked for playing
the disappointed pastor, for mixing religion and medicine, science and faith. He has been criticized for a fundamental defect of method, for intellectual and practical error: "This is
not to be taken seriously." Worse yet, a common complaint is
that his method is an abuse of the patient and of the medical
profession.

The critical judgment of an unforewarned and, in addition,
unbelieving foreign visitor would undoubtedly be shocked by
the purpose, content, and form of our work and by the very
psychology of certain participants. In fact, I would go so far
as to say that his intellectual honesty, the natural honesty of the
patient and of the physician, would be shocked. Such a person will be annoyed, as though a dishonest act were being performed before him or as if he were being presented with
counterfeit merchandise. Is not some other commodity being
circulated under the pretense of practicing medicine, i.e., the
commodity of the apostolate, of religious preaching, of apologetic? The feeling of fraud is twofold: the deceiving of others
is coupled, in effect, with self-deception.

Let us state flatly the reaction of the visitor: "Has not the
Medicine of the Person remained in, or relapsed into, the
mythical stage (or into the metaphysical oppressions) of human evolution? Is it not necessary to help it rise to the positive
stage of medicine?" This seems elementary, and the visitor
blushes to have to recall it, to recall, in short, what several
centuries of cultural maturation have definitely established for
us. The visitor wonders if it is necessary to begin everything

over. We physicians of the person, it is said, carried by the excessive zeal of a faith (which the visitor respects), are behind the times in this age of electronics. We claim to be the precursors, but are relegated to the ranks of faith healers and miracle workers, of visionaries with confused ideas.

We do not seek to deny that this is the feeling of unbelieving visitors (I am not talking about that grain of intolerance which works its way into the most highly polished mechanism of a scientific intellect). Nor do we seek to deny that this is even the reaction of physicians who are Christians, but who are concerned not to "mix species" (although they admit certain critical points of contact). Finally, we would not deny that this is one of the major difficulties and stumbling blocks of the Medicine of the Person.

On the contrary, it is only fair (and good method), especially for a Latin spirit, to state and confront objections squarely, even in their language and on their own ground. In any case, it is important to define things clearly at the outset of such a work as the present one, and to elucidate as we proceed.

But let us begin with some general methodological remarks, after which I will attempt to indicate the meaning and limits of the Medicine of the Person.

III

Positivism, understood as a respect for facts of observation and as a respect for the impersonal objectivity of fact, constitutes one of the major attainments of modern history. Yet it should be added that, since the nineteenth century, scientific thought, *through a critique of the scientific fact itself*, has realized the importance of ideas of history and of totality. Through the analysis of what is apparently the most simple fact of observation, scientific thought has seen the interaction between the observer and the thing observed.

This is a decisive revolution. It is explained, in the first place, by the pressure of the biological fact and, even more, of the psychosociological fact, on mental habits adapted to physico-chemical models (themselves previously outlined from mathematical models). But this revolution, based on the originality of the anthropological fact, receives its logic from the physical sciences. The idea of pure objectivity is universally disparaged, to make room for the subject-object idea. Wherever the subject apparently faded into the background in order to make it possible for the bare, *im*personal fact to speak, analysis now reveals that the subject is still implied in things, as things are implied in the subject.

Such considerations have not served to simplify our tasks. On the contrary, we would even say that they have condemned the simplification of approaches in favor of " immediate complexity." Instead of progressing step by step from the simple to the complex, which would be more economical, and instead of reducing by degrees the complex to the simple, the unknown to the known, the process has been reversed. The less is explained by the more, the letter by the word, the sentence by the total meaning of the speech, the reflex arc by a world-defining structural totality, the elemental movements by global behavior.

Why is this so? We are convinced that the simple fact, obtained by analysis or experimentation, is only an artifice. It is a fragment artificially isolated from the whole. Thus, under the pretense of respecting the thing-in-itself, the thing-in-itself is betrayed through a manipulation that is nothing more than a violation of it. The scientist has created abnormal, pathological, partial, and tendentious conditions, while laboring under the delusion concerning the objectivity of the facts he puts forth.

The only concern in scientific observations of *facts* was that one beware of the " facts " thus obtained, that one be aware of the alternative and constructive part played by the observer, i.e., the subject. These " facts " were not *facts,* and the respect for *facts* meant going beyond " facts." That is, what was needed was that the part of the subject who apprehends be made clearer. What was needed, above all, was a restoration of the fact to the totality of reality from which our analytic spirit had abusively extracted it.

In sum, that which Positivism took for facts was merely the product of our operations. That which it fanatically defended in the name of objectivity was not something objective, but was really unrecognized subjectivity, or at least a mixed subject-object, an observer-observed pair. Thus it was necessary to go beyond Positivism in the name of Positivism itself.

A twofold progress has been made in this matter. On the one hand, the degree of presence of a subject in the scientific object has been made clearer; the partial and one-sided character of this object has been recognized. On the other hand, the object has been reintegrated into the total fabric of reality. This twofold progress has been carried out in physics under Einstein, and even more in biology and medicine. Finally, it has been elucidated by Husserlian phenomenology, which replaces explicative and reductive analysis with a concern for integral comprehension (through the reductions themselves per se) of the fabric of the world in its indissoluble unity.

IV

This conversion of the modern scholar vis-à-vis general anthropological concepts is still more dramatic. In proof of this, outside the field of medicine, I would cite only the revolution introduced into political economy and sociology by Marxist analysis. It seems to me that such an example is all the more significant in that it deeply marks our age and permits useful confrontations with our own terrain. Even more, it is situated in what is commonly called atheistic materialism, apparently the opposite of our own spiritual heritage.

Marxist analyses have, indeed, definitively unmasked the false objectivity, the false neutrality of scientific naturalism. In regard to economics, such naturalism isolates the market exchanges from human projects and from the political and ethical presuppositions behind those exchanges.

True scientific objectivity is obtained, first of all, by laying bare these "subjective" presuppositions, whatever they may be, that lay behind the deceptive serenity of statistics. This objectivity consists in recognizing and taking into account the inevitably subjective, philosophical, ethical, political, and militant character of all science.

The notion of *praxis* corrects all pseudoneutrality of a description, no matter how abstract and aloof from jumbled reality such a description is considered. For example, is not a historical description oriented by the way in which it has been defined, outlined, and situated? Take the most innocent facts found in the public archives (ignoring any critique of the witness of these archives themselves): the mere action of appropriating them as *facts* pushes them into the spotlight. This is done through the partial magic of the observer's attention, of his perspective and of the mentality of his age. He renders insignificant things significant, and vice versa.

All science is perspectivist. It can disengage itself from its perspectives only by untiringly clarifying them.

This is an inexhaustible task, for everything we do is oriented. We are involved in each thing. Properly speaking, there is no scientific object; there are only cultural objects. These objects are betrayed in one sense, made fruitful and meaningful in another sense, by our settled prejudices.

A neopositivism recognizes a real objectivity beyond any oversimplified pseudo-objectivity. This real objectivity is *initial* in the project of objectivity and *terminal* in the infinite task of explaining the interrelationships found in the subject-object-history-totality complex that makes up the most harmless fact.

V

We have spoken of economics and history. The experience is identical in philosophy: "There is no philosophy without presuppositions," writes Paul Ricoeur.[2] " It wants to be *Thought* with its presuppositions. . . . Its honesty is in making clear its presuppositions, in stating them as belief, in elaborating the belief as wager and an attempt to recover its wager in comprehension. Such a wager is the exact opposite of an apologetic." [3]

I want to exhibit these very presuppositions, this same wager. Each of us, as physicians or as patients, must daily be conscious of these presuppositions and be responsible for them.

First of all, in medicine as in economics, history, or physics, there is no compartmentalizing nosology without inevitable deception. All our organic diseases are rough approximations that trap us by their simplicity: " Disease is not some part in man; it resides neither in an organ nor in a separate function: it constitutes a mobilization and reorganization of the entire individual." [4]

Thus we discover here, as elsewhere, the illusory objectivity of biological " facts," such as the perspective of the observer or the theory of the moment isolates them. We discover also an individual and transindividual totality, that is, a person in his relationships with the world, of which diseases express the maladjustments.

At the same time, there is a discovery of my perspectives as perspectives, my biases as biases. *The physician learns that he himself is situated,* that his medicine is inevitably situated. He understands and applies his medicine according to certain coordinates that have been taught him. His way of understanding and acting inevitably reflects the static or dynamic organicism of his anatomo- or physio-pathologist teachers. His way of understanding and acting expresses his culture, his middle or lower class origins, his beliefs, his way of accepting or refusing life, his moral and religious convictions.

It would be false to say that the nonbeliever is objective, whereas the believer is biased. What is true for one is true for the other.[5] It would be inexact to claim that, believer or not, only the physician who *abstracts* his belief is objective, whereas the one who does not abstract his belief is not objective. Neither of them is objective, or perhaps they are both objective in the same degree. Both have dissected the wholeness of reality. Both have made a choice and have inflicted a wound, for to make an *abstraction* is to do *violence*.

The nonbeliever in no wise has a monopoly on objectivity, on *neutrality*. He has his "superstructures" like everybody else. He imposes his particular perspective on reality. The time is past when the only language considered to have philosophic value (i.e., the value of universality) was that of a secularized rationalism continued in an insipid deism. The neutrality of the "first principle of the Universe" is a pseudo-neutrality. Today *it is no longer assumed that the absence of a given perspective is the absence of perspective*. Perspective is everywhere, and especially there where it is not acknowledged.

As for the believer, and for the same reasons, it is no longer assumed that *the setting-in-parentheses of one's faith grants him a monopoly on objectivity*. It is no longer taken for granted that this whitewashes every settled prejudice, procuring for the believer a certificate of purity. Choice and perspective still remain, as do violence and bias.

It is even to be feared that a distortion particularly prejudicial to the truth and efficacy of his medical thought and practice is introduced by this "setting-in-parentheses" (which quarantines for the believer — if he is really believing — that which makes up the very foundation of his everyday life). What do diagnosis and therapeutics become once this permanent mental restriction has mutilated them? Is one not frightened by the cadaver of a medicine thus manipulated? At least, one would be frightened if one were aware of what an authentic faith really means.

If such a quarantining of his faith normally causes no difficulty for the physician, it is due to one of two things. Either he has kept only a semblance of faith, or else he has fallen victim to an abstract pseudopositivism that has literally distorted his medicine to the point where he no longer understands anything except affections of the lungs, of the liver, of the vertebrae — items of illness without life and without soul. At a congress of Catholic physicians held in Paris, in October, 1959, one of the most brilliant of the participants exclaimed from the rostrum, " The only concept I acknowledge is mathematics."

This mentality, which is called scientific, is certainly still current in our time. Nevertheless, at the same time and in the same area the importance of the problems of life in sickness and healing is being underlined through a criticism of the pigeon-holing organicist.

Now, *the same criticism* that requires going beyond the mere collection of statistics or organs in order to aim at the total person requires *ipso facto* that faith not be abstracted when it exists in the patient or in the physician. The same concern for the person and for totality forbids cutting off the illness (as well as the therapeutic action) from its moral and religious dimensions.

The study of transference and countertransference, or in any case the importance of the patient-physician relationship, renders more urgent than ever the analysis, and the self-analysis, of the physician. It is not a matter of indifference (in the eyes of the least heretical analyst) whether or not a given practitioner be a believer, whether or not he make an abstraction of his faith, causing violence, etc. Nor is it a matter of indifference whether or not the medicine practiced on a patient indulge in operations of the " abstracting " type, etc.

In any case, one is " involved " and one " involves " his patient, whether one likes it or not, whether one says it or just keeps quiet about it.[6] Thus it is just as well not to keep quiet, but to admit this involvement to introduce some clarity into the sometimes ill-defined zone (which is always unclear in other respects) between the patient and the physician.

To sum up, I would say that it is necessary to dispel two

illusions. The first is that a *neutral position* (in medicine as elsewhere) is possible, into which we could withdraw, secure from all compromise with conscience, to the condition of "leaving it alone." Thus, for instance, we have the physician who prudently remains at the portal of his patient's life, from fear of having to lay aside his purely medical role.

The second illusion is that of believing that one can practice what is called a "psychotherapy" without "getting wet," i.e., that one can remain in this position of "*neutrality*" (which we have just seen is *not* neutral). The physician must realize that he is entirely involved in his treatment, whether he likes it or not. This is true even though this involvement is carefully avoided, so to speak, in the traditional, nonanalytic psychotherapies. In such psychotherapies the physician stands *objectively* before his patient, distinct from his therapy. His therapy remains a purely objective technique: counsel, tranquilizers, training, etc. He continues as part of the objective order. He keeps himself free from his prescriptions, remaining tranquil and satisfied, "beyond influence." This is a therapy of "nonengagement."

On the contrary, not only in psychotherapy, but even more in every therapy where the physician "is himself prescribed" (Balint), *it is the therepeutic relationship itself which becomes therapy:* it is not *what* I say or prescribe (the operation of the object), but our personal, inexpressible intersubjectivity as such. Thus, in this case, I must learn to give myself as therapeutic nourishment. This is to recognize at what point the transformation and purification of the physician are essential (in the moral and in the analytic meanings of the term) in a prescription that is in reality an increasing, reciprocating transformation of persons. Under these conditions it is obvious that it is not a question of setting in parentheses the religious attitude of either the patient or the physician.

VI

What I have just said *does not* mean that the Medicine of
the Person consists of "converting" people, of healing them
by a more or less openly "religious" type of conversion. We
want to leave no doubt about that.

The Medicine of the Person is not a spiritual form of psychotherapy. It is not a method or technique of approaching the
sick person, but an attitude and a *spirit* that are beyond all
medical techniques (in particular, psychotherapy) and are
therefore not counted among them.

This is not to say that the Medicine of the Person begins
where the techniques end. Although they are contemporaneous, they are not of the same order.

Perhaps we can profit from this remark to make a little more
precise the modes of application of the Medicine of the Person in its relations with psychotherapy, on the one hand, and
religious faith on the other.

A. The Medicine of the Person is not a psychotherapeutic
"specialty," [7] a religious psychotherapy. It is even possible, in
certain cases, to be a physician of the person without ever
having learned or practiced psychotherapy. This comes
through that presence, tact, and love which have no need of
words to reveal the person behind the patient, behind the
"case," the grippe, the fracture, the incurable, or the dying.
Consequently, "life's problems" and neuroses, which seemingly belong to the psychologist, are rather of a nature that
blurs the distinction between a technique and a *spirit*.

The Medicine of the Person does not identify itself with any
particular psychotherapeutic efficacy (and even less with a
religious one). Nevertheless, in the final analysis it is mani-
fested in an efficacy of a psychotherapeutic nature which it
has inspired in the first place (let us not confuse motivation
with instrumentality). It forces me to become a psychotherapist and to acquaint myself with psychological techniques. It
pushes me to the difficult, imprudent, and dangerous risk of

the psychotherapeutic approach to my everyday patients (an approach which, frankly, I could do without under the present conditions of medical practice).

The cares previously called "life's problems," which are apparently the most typical, in reality seem to be among the most "deceptive." Illnesses that are the most trivial in appearance can reveal to the physician of the person a problem of life, because he will have been looking for it.

The often invoked contradistinction between that which is "private" in a sick person and that which is "personal" to him would formulate differently what I have just stated. Some people call "private" those facts which, in my life or in the life of the patient, do not concern other people. These facts are described as being unimportant and insignificant. They are of no interest to what is essential in our therapeutic relationships. And it is added: I have no need for the patient to lay himself open before me, nor for me to do the same before him, in order to come to a personal relationship that goes much farther and much deeper, even to the essentials (which the term "private," on the contrary, evades and disguises). How many confidences, willingly related in detail, soon act swiftly to block the way to a great and unique confession!

This is undoubtedly true. However, we should be careful that "private" does not become a respectable name for indifference. That which is "private" to an inattentive, hurried, egoistic, or timid physician (these being substitutes for discretion), becomes "personal" to the physician of the person, who endeavors to read with love the profound problem behind that which is petty, ridiculous, and "embarrassing" in a "private" confidence. The terms "personal" and "private" express less the type of confession than the attention of him who receives it.

In summary, although not identifying itself with a psychotherapy, the Medicine of the Person does not therefore scorn, it goes without saying, the psychotherapeutic tool. For the Medicine of the Person to be reabsorbed into psychotherapy would be for it to fall back into an objective technique. The great danger of all psychotherapies that are occupied with the patient-subject instead of the patient-object consists of treating the subject in its turn in the manner of an object.[8]

B. In regard to the subject of the person, how do we situate that special intervention (among others) that consists of making the patient grasp the fact that he is the prisoner of a certain attitude toward life, that he must liberate himself if he wants to be healed, that all healing worthy of the name could not ignore this liberation, and that, finally, we are in the love of God?

First of all, we should emphasize that this type of intervention is not at all the same as a religious discourse, and that one can very well penetrate to the heart of a sick person with the eyes of faith without ever speaking of faith. Such a distinction seems to me to be essential: its misappreciation would wholly compromise both our relationship with the patient and the future of the Medicine of the Person.

Thus it is one thing to act under the inspiration of God and another thing to speak of it. These are different, and often they are contraries. Here we cannot emphasize enough the importance of that *religious modesty* that one is always in danger of offending in his neighbor if God is spoken of too indiscreetly.

Perhaps it will be said that this is a matter of mood, of breeding. One must have the courage to go beyond a certain fear of public opinion, to dare to call oneself Christian and to mention the name of Christ! This is true. But we should not forget the religious modesty of our interlocutors. If we do, we could very well end up with the opposite of the desired result in our effort of communication. It is well known to what point explicit religion can constitute an obstacle to the genuine experience of God. And it is with the unbeliever that the physician of the person sometimes feels the most at ease. To speak as little as possible of so-called spiritual things, and *always in the very language of the other* — this is part of the respect for the person and for the truth (and efficacy) of the Medicine of the Person.

The basic duty is *discretion*, which is coupled with the classic rule of the "neutrality" of the physician and of the psychotherapist. It would be disastrous to confuse the Medicine of the Person with a certain form of spiritual or religious interference. I would say that the rule for the physician of the person is that of *neutrality* in the sense of discretion and tactfulness, of infinite respect for others. This is not to contradict what I said before regarding the falseness of a neutrality on the deeper level of our manner of being and acting, a neutrality of segregation or abstraction, a sham neutrality, which is as far from the other as indifference is from love.

The form of our intervention in the spiritual life of a patient, when it seems of direct interest in his illness, will therefore be of an extreme *prudence*. This prudence will not exclude the audacity and the imprudence of a saving inspiration at the crucial moment required by the liberation, i.e., by the healing of the sick person. Prudence and imprudence, like the psychological and the spiritual, are not on the same plane.

This would not involve taking the place of a spiritual director (a charge leveled at Paul Tournier), to whom one will most frequently refer the patient for religious problems. Thus a judicious collaboration will keep us from playing poorly a role that belongs to others more competent. However, this will depend on the patient's submitting to it himself. It must not be a covert avoidance on the physician's part. Finally, the authority and habit of the priest must in no wise result in a psychospiritual collapse.

Indeed, there are cases where the priest (as such) will play this therapeutic role less effectively than a physician, for the inverse reason of the "officially" spiritual nature of his intervention. Some "unbelieving" patients "would prefer not to hear it discussed." Their problem of life is indeed religious, but of an embryonic religion which obstinately rejects the title. It is up to the physician to know how to bring the patient's awareness to the same level as his problem and to show that his anxiety and his problem are coeval. To refer it immediately to the priest would be to put the cart before the horse.

This is an ambiguous area, difficult to define, and one that ordinarily is no longer called medicine. Since there is always a danger of drifting off into spiritual direction, it is a delicate therapeutic undertaking. The frontier is surely displaced and imprecise. As with all things that no longer touch technical, abstract problems but concrete problems of life, the physician of the person must feel his way along carefully. It must be left to his spirit of finesse, to his own spiritual impulses.

As I have often stated, if our meddling in the ethicospiritual domain of our patients is feared, it is because of the danger of an unauthorized *value judgment*. Such an unauthorized judgment would harmfully render the patient guilty by confusing sickness with sin.

We do not want to anticipate, in this introductory chapter, a problem that will perhaps have to be raised later. However, it should be well understood that, on this point, the *neutrality* of the physician of the person will be total, with no possible restrictions. This is true whatever be his convictions, and even if a link could sometimes be presupposed between sin and sickness. The physician has no more right than anyone else to assume that which is God's. Sin is not the concern of the physician.

If the patient discovers, for example, an attitude of pride or resentment at the root of his neurosis, we must accept this sign, this symptom, as such. This is not a moral judgment. It is a psychological ascertainment and diagnosis of a *moral conduct*. "You are living under the influence of guilt" is not at all a judgment of guilt ("You are guilty"). To accept and recognize with the patient that pride is at the source of his illness does not have the same repercussions in the physician's office that it has in some confessionals.

I would add, however, that of the two ways of applying the precept: "Thou shalt not judge," the most neutral of the two is not always the one we think. Sometimes it is already a lack of "neutrality" to bring the patient to an understanding and an admission that an *attitude of guiltiness* is present in place of real sin. There are some types of exculpation that are oppressive in the direction of determinism, of fate. When a Marxist or a bourgeois psychoanalyst says that he *understands* me and that my opinion or my attitude is not at all culpable, that it reflects or repeats only my unhappy childhood or my class, he does not liberate me. Rather, he weighs me down even more.

In this way the neutrality of the scientific or psychoanalytic type is doubly overburdening, both through the impassibility of the clinician (who, in a way, lays himself bare: "It is not my role to take that into account") and through the very exculpation of the patient, who falls from sin into something even worse: he diagnoses himself and judges himself sick from guiltiness.

The stating of sin as such often delivers and heals better than its metamorphosis into a symptom. And the only liberating neutrality is that of *charity*, whether one is a physician or not. Being a physician does not exempt one from being a person in the presence of persons.

There are two neutralities, and I could not say which one is the most neutral and respects more the rule of not judging. The one declares: "You have imagined your sin of pride (or your pride as sin); you have made yourself the prisoner of the prejudices of an education." The other states: "We are all prideful, but certain people have learned, as I have, that we are forgiven our prideful nature." These two neutralities are not mutually exclusive, and one will sometimes be the loser when the other fulfills its liberating function. Without this discernment and this respect for the conscience of the other, I would not be a physician of the person, and I would not be "neutral." True neutrality is this discernment and this respect.

In any case, and I repeat, the Medicine of the Person is not a procedure but an inspiration. One can practice it without ever entering into ethical and spiritual problems as such. One can approach them indirectly. It is not a specialty or a particular technique. It does not need to avoid or use sparingly the ordinary medical techniques.

Indeed, I would like to end my remarks by dealing with an unjustified reproach that could be leveled at the Medicine of the Person. It might be objected that we take lightly our experiments by trial and error, our dilatoriness, the difficulties of our techniques, our purely human interventions. This, it might be said, is a cheap optimism, this optimism of the "magicians of the person" (thanks to the inspiration of the Holy Spirit).

To be sure, the "person" can serve as an alibi, giving us a good conscience that is forgetful of the grossly materialistic, economic, and political interventions so typical of the practice of medicine in both the bourgeois countries of "commercial expansion" and in the "underdeveloped" countries. I would hope that the positions I have recently taken will allow me to escape such suspicions.[9] If there is still some doubt remaining on this score, I would like to dispose of it here and now by emphasizing the urgent necessity of technical interventions, as a matter of course.[10] We must be quite severe against an "all-around Personalism." I repeat again that the Medicine of the Person is not intended to be a substitute for any type of medicine. *It is not a medicine; it is the spirit in which medicine is practiced.*

VII

But does it suffice to show that the pseudo-objectivity, formerly called scientific, is still and always a perspective, a point of view on the object (evidence for which, in general, cannot be doubted)? Is it enough to show that this rationalism is irrational, that this objectivism is subjectivist?

Perhaps we should go farther and, while untiringly disclosing our perspectives as such, show how one could attempt to leave the enchanted circle of "points of view," as the satellite escapes gravitation, in order to place ourselves in the orbit of a "point of view that is no longer one" — the point of view of totality itself.[11] For this it would be necessary to bring about a *realignment*, to effect a decisive *conversion*. We would need to shift poles and to jump from the point of view of the "englobed" to that of the *englobing* (Jaspers).

Now, what can we call this realignment, this conversion to a total view that is no longer "objective" nor perspectivist, unless we call it "religious" conversion (in the widest sense of the term).

I could not better illustrate this going beyond, this absolute reversal of a point of view toward the *direction* of an englobing, than to take as an *example* the Pauline reversal from *Christ-as-point-of-view* (as one religion among others in the world) to Christ as totality. It is no longer Christ in the world; it is the world that is in Christ. This is to say that the point of reference from now on is not my particular point of view, but the point of view that is not numbered among the others. It is not that point of view which I give, but the one which is given to me, which is revealed to me. To rise beyond my individual self in this way is possible, as a matter of fact, only through a *revelation*, and by the help of the Spirit.

Thus I agree to leave my point of view, for which (to continue the example) God and Christ are problems, one problem among others, a topic for discussion and appraisal: What does Christ bring to the world; what must be expected from him; what place does he occupy among man's preoccupations? How is he justified in the eyes of reason and philosophy? And so on. I acquiesce in realigning myself. I make a choice. It is an *Other* who fixes my attention. It is not a particular *Other* (that would be to alienate my attention instead of liberating it), but the absolute and absolutely inward *Other* (transcendent and immanent, as theology puts it), the *Other* in whom I am fulfilled and who is the fulfillment of history.

There are two reasons why we could not "demonstrate" that Christianity leads such a realignment to its goal and fulfillment (which is attainable, in their own measure, by all religions, among which, as a total vision, Marxism would have its place):

1. Every demonstration seizes hold of the interlocutor as if he were an adversary. There is a totalitarianism of rational demonstration that does not suit the very roots of choice, of the total meaning of existence. This area involves *at most* a witnessing.

2. Since every demonstration is of a discursive nature, it necessarily borrows the very language of objectivity, the language of "points of view," which in this case it would be the mission of the demonstration to challenge. Such a perplexity is vicious, in that it constrains me to formulate another method while utilizing the material, language, and logic of exactly that method which I am challenging. No other material is available with which to challenge this same material. Demonstration, if it were possible in this case, would be the living negation of that which it would intend to show, namely, something beyond all demonstration and all perspectivist language.

Bergson said that the champion of liberty is always wrong in a philosophic debate (where the adversary utilizes rational demonstration), but that time plays in the favor of the champion of liberty. One must know how to wait. The other, during this time, matures. Exactly, the point of view (which is not one) of totality, which situates me in Christ, does not assert itself except in slowly working itself out in the world and in history, a working out that has its finish only at the end of time. The perspectiveless goal is eschatological. As with all *praxis*, it is "demonstrated" only in being revealed, in being fulfilled (by means of words, medical practice, example, etc.); it is fulfilled only progressively and bears fruit at the end of history. This fulfillment is perfect in the sense that it embraces history *and* each individual person.

The term "demonstration" is inadequate here. That which is required (beyond a *critique* of the "objective" point of view) is a dividing of this goal of totality that carries us to the other pole, to the point of view that is no longer a point of view. Some humility is needed in order to accept the fact that objectivity is subjective, and that that which one ordinarily condescendingly calls subjectivity is the way of absolute objectivity. I acquiesce in leaving the former, which I called "the objective observation of facts," because I took myself for the center of perspective. I no longer take myself as the center of the universe and cease being the absolute center of perspective. Our colleague and friend Karlfried Graf von Dürckheim explores the depths of an analogous undertaking when he tries to have the patient share the experience of transcendence. In order to test this reversal by which I detach myself from my "small self," discourse must leave room for witness (to continue the example).

Is this to say that "discourse" does not have a place beyond an "objective" (i.e., perspectivist) anthropology? Is it to say that one cannot attempt to force language to express the fact that there is in no wise an existential (i.e., concrete, historical, and personal) anthropology without Christ? Such discourse underlies the principal Christian philosophies, which are situated and centered in Christ, yet which do not always explicitly give the logic of their philosophic universe. Is it not possible to force such an option of faith to speak, to make itself explicit in the obviously inadequate language of a methodology? In Descartes and Spinoza, totality is reintroduced at the end, as if they turned Saint Augustine upside down, after having begun with certain rational premises.

But our aim is not to elaborate a Christian anthropology. We will skirt its territory through one of its detours, the study of the body and its meaning.

VIII

Before I proceed, I must explain myself on an equivocation that will undoubtedly appear throughout the work. I appeal to a religious option, to a Christian option, and I do so *some-*

times from the inside and sometimes from the outside. Not every transcendence is religious, nor is every approach that engages me totally. The equivocation is: Do I call upon the Christian faith as an example (among other attitudes analogous to the Christian faith), or do I predicate it as a prerequisite to a human (and medical) comprehension and practice capable of progressing to the end of their logic?

It would be futile to sidestep a difficulty marking our work in the Medicine of the Person, for otherwise it can misrepresent the fluctuations of a Christian life lacking assurance and truth. It would be wrong to give one's blessing to a certain woolliness of thought and expression, by baptizing it with the fine name of "broad-mindedness," when it reflects quite a different thing, namely, the blemish of irresolution in my very life. My language is the man that I am. Our language is also in the image of our age and our culture, which are no longer certain of being the only ones right, in splendid ignorance of what is true in other ages and cultures. We are conscious of being a challenged minority; yet, on the other hand, we have not gained universal adherence through compromising our convictions. We are between two cripples.

As a disciple of Jesus Christ, I take on an air of intransigence. I risk cutting certain bridges. Yet there is nothing of "intolerance" in this attitude. My choices are made clearly explicit, as such. And far from challenging others by this, I give myself over to the uncomfortable precariousness of a language that I am aware is suspect and perhaps even rejected.

If, on the other hand, I try to make myself accept the greatest number of propositions, then I must make my own propositions relative. I must propose them as examples, giving them a more general, less direct, and less forceful orientation.

Is this a regrettable wavering between the imperious demands of a faith of compelling truth and patent concessions to the varied convictions of others? I do not think so. The more I can become closer to Christ, the more I will be closer to him who does not bear the name of Christian.

In the same way, I think that this lameness of our world and of my life can teach us something. I would not want to homogenize at any cost that which is heterogeneous, but I cannot see a division between the broad and imprecise understanding of conversion (let us say "religious") and a narrow understanding of it (for us, "Christian"); between the sense of transcendence "beyond religions" (of our friend von Dürckheim) and faith in Jesus Christ. It is "within" for one, "beyond" for another, but both are of the same order. Between narrow understanding and broad understanding, there is undoubtedly the unavoidable sudden transition and discontinuity of a conversion. But there is also a kinship and harmony in the attitude of every man who is not short-circuited in the metaphysical narcissism of self-conceit; on the contrary, he becomes attentive, obeying a verity that *transcends* him.

The sense of transcendence is not faith in Jesus Christ. It is not even a specifically or "officially" religious attitude. But it follows the same furrow, and in spite of everything, I see there only a more or less advanced degree (despite discontinuities and conversions) of differentiation (better than *development* or *deepening*). Whether or not we call *religious* the option that places man in a totality and makes him attentive to a call whose source he does not understand, it is nonetheless a matter of the same goal, of the same trajectory prolonged more or less distant, arrested or diverted. One need only follow the dotted line to make this curve coincide with the most complete expression of faith (e.g., catholic).

What appears true for one is a fortiori for another. On the other hand, the faith that represents for me the *completion* (fulfillment) of the religious trajectory will not be accepted as such by others: inhabiting the "common trunk" of the goal, they will say "beyond" (and not "within") a contingent religious position. But in any case, the relationship of implication and of interlocking remains.

I should add that this language, which I call the most differentiated (and the most compromising) of languages, can have nothing of exclusiveness, of monopoly, of exclusion, of "private property" about it. Every religion, under whatever name, is an approach to Him who has for us the name of Christ. Every *total* option, even when it calls itself atheism, is in the line of religious conversion.[12]

I have made my "wager"; I have chosen my language. Yet nevertheless I must speak the language of all; I must reincorporate the language of others. I can take the liberty of playing on two keyboards, if I clearly inform the reader of my intention. Two ways are open to me. One is of the less differentiated language, common to us all. The other is that of the more specialized language, which no doubt requires of the non-Christian reader an effort of accommodation and of conversion (of the attention), which is the very thing required of me when I come forward to meet him in order to identify myself with him. It is a condition of reciprocity.

In a nonspecialized work such as the present one, I have not wished to exclude either of the ways at first. It will be essential that one not serve as an evasion or denial of the other. In the midst of any such effort of reciprocal comprehension, it is not certain that the undifferentiated nature of a "neutral" or neutralized language is the most favorable for a veritable communion. Let each one thoroughly examine its option, toward the maximum of differentiation. Let each discover a little better its difference; the divergences will be accentuated only at first sight and superficially. If one is a good listener, that which alienates at first can, if the route is pursued, bring together again and cement even more a true comradeship of arms.

IX

Such, then, preliminarily stated in detail, are the "neopositivistic" coordinates, so to speak, that orient this work on the body. Let us repeat that we are not breaking with a quite prevalent current of thought which, through a concern for a complete approach to a sector of reality, "mixes species" (to the disgust of the logicoanalytic grammarians of classical positivism). It is not at all a matter of a specifically religious current, but it contains the same principle, and the religious current furnishes one specification of it.

If the reader wants to enter sympathetically into the text, i.e., to understand it, he will not forget the terms of the method. The nonbeliever will set for himself the effort of a contextual reading of the text.

For my part, I will try my best to utilize a language as general as possible. This is not easy in an area where the references having the most meaning can also be the most disturbing. In following this course, I will be careful to facilitate the acceptance of terms and assertions. It is true that the difficulties of vocabulary are never exhausted, even between collaborators yoked to the same task for a long period of time.

This being said, what goal are we pursuing and what would be the place of a reflection on corporeality in the ensemble of an anthropology at which we are working as a group? Our practical goal would be to contribute to the conversion of physicians and of the public to a different form of medicine. This medicine is more complete and more effective than that practiced not only by the out-of-date apostles of organic medicine, but also by psychosomaticians, psychiatrists, and psychoanalysts. Our contribution to their conversion would consist in carrying forward their own beginnings. For example, Balint's work on the psychotherapeutic possibilities of the practitioner through the formation of groups is a work that is precious to us. We must unite our efforts to increase in our countries the number of seminars analogous to that of Balint.[13] Nothing could hope to replace the example of each practitioner plunging in and putting into practice the Medicine of the Person. Nothing replaces daily experience, contacts, failures, and experimentation.

But the exact case that one brings to debate is carried on in teaching; in the same way, a doctrinal reflection clarifies and consolidates fieldwork. *Praxis* is approached from both sides.

It is incontestable that light projected on the exact meaning of an illness and healing can lead the physician and the patient to a decisive awareness, to a conversion of their relationships and their behavior regarding an affection. It can lead to a therapeutic change, to a different orientation of the healing effort. For example, it can replace the " assisting " antibiotic with a better attitude of the body and the spirit.

We have referred to a better attitude. The importance of attitude in the genesis and healing of illnesses is well known. It is well known, but rarely enough taken into account. A consideration of the meaning of the body and of its attitudes must lead to this being taken into account in medical practice.

The Medicine of the Person keeps us from remaining *veterinarians,* as Auguste Comte put it, limited by the body of our patients. We cannot overemphasize the part played by the psychological and the spiritual in the most indisputably lesional affections.

But if we reject, or seem to reject in this manner, a medicine limited by the body, *is it not because we have not grasped the true meaning of the body?* If the body were something more and other than what the anatomist fancies, then a medicine of the body in the total sense of the word could be nothing other than a medicine of the total person.

If, then, we appear as " soul-hawkers " within the very gates of technolatry (insofar as we are ready to laugh in the faces of the organicists for whom all that we claim is " philosophical " or some puerile moralism), it is perhaps because neither side has understood the meaning of the body of the child, the body of the woman, and the body of the aged, the sick body or the healthy body.

This reconsideration of the body, to which I invite you, will not then be for us the preservation of an angelism forgetful of organic conditioning; even less will it be the opposite, i.e., a repetition that the body is not everything, that its illnesses overlay problems of the " soul," that sickness is only the visible face of an invisible problem, and other obvious facts repeated over and over again in our day.

No, it is not a question of ignoring (or of avoiding ignoring) or of recalling or of flattering the body. Rather, it is a question of understanding what it *means,* of understanding *it,* of examining much more thoroughly the mystery of our *corporeality* and the mystery of our *incarnation,* i.e., in sum, of our *personal existence.*

Our purpose is to aid physicians and patients to comprehend the meaning of the body and to live it. This means:

1. that the physician will undoubtedly commit himself to comprehending the true meaning of the sick body in his patients;

2. but that he will commit himself also to comprehending the way in which the patient himself comprehends it;

3. and consequently, of teaching him to comprehend it better;

4. that, finally, in comprehending it better the patient will thus learn to become the master of his sick body, to be reconciled to it, in short, to be healed, to gain health.

To comprehend the meaning of our corporeality is to take the first steps toward healing, toward health; it is to do a concrete work of total health; it is to do a medical work.

The converse is also true and contains a profound maxim: to be restored to health or to maintain oneself in good health is a way (implicit and hidden, to be sure, but without false modesty) of comprehending the true meaning of the body.

" To fit neatly into one's skin " is the way the French put it: *to fulfill, to bring to accomplishment* one's life in its plenitude, i.e., at the same time and in the same movement to have understood life, body, and spirit. To understand them is to live on good terms with them (as one *understands* a friend). To understand the true meaning of the body is to love it, to live in friendship with it.

On the other hand, I will endeavor to show in this book, intended for physicians as well as for patients, that it is the same thing *to betray the body* (through inopportune contempt, rebellion, idealism and or materialism) and *to betray our most spiritual being that we call the person,* in its most universal dimensions on the world's scale and in its most eternal dimensions in the eyes of God.

I will try to show how it is the same thing to betray the body and to idolize the body, how it is one and the same thing to love or respect my body and to locate it or go beyond it, that is, *to read the meaning of the body through its appearance.*

Sickness is a code that we must know how to decipher. To discover its hidden meaning, what it signifies, is to translate, in a way, the message that the patient addresses to his surroundings through the mediation of the malaise or lesion. All psychologists are aware of this. Indeed, our body as a whole is also the coded language through which we manifest ourselves, healthy or sick. Through it we send our messages. Through it, the real " us " is expressed, a great deal more than we realize or would wish.

But there is even more. I will repeat throughout these pages that our body reveals both our problems and our resources: not *only* our problems, but *also our resources.* Our problems are the messages that we address, the questions that we put to the world. But our resources are also important, in that they correspond to the questions that are put to us. Of what are we capable?

These are the two directions: the question or message that we express; the question or message that is expressed to us. Our body is a *sign* through which we make known and through which something is made known to us. This something which is required of us is simply our vocation. The body is perhaps the language by which God interrogates us.

PART ONE

BODY–OBJECT AND BODY–SUBJECT

CHAPTER I

The Birth of a Segregation of the Body

I

JEAN-PAUL SARTRE, IN REACTING ALONG WITH OTHERS AGAINST the partitioning of the body, which breaks the original and global feeling of our existence, wrote: "I *exist* my body." [14] For the philosopher the question is one of tracing back an ineluctable current that has brought man and civilization to *maturity*. However, in the innocence one imagines to be present in the infant and in primeval man, it is so simple to be one's body. And the same is true for a person in full action and sound health, if he is observed unaware. Such a person thinks of everything *but* his organs. He unconsciously enjoys living, self-abandon, even wasting his energies.

The body is more than a commodious instrument that I could do without: my body is myself, the man who I am. Think, for example, of the well-trained athlete or of a beautiful girl. Consider the worth of their bodies. The girl's body really belongs to her, or rather, it is herself. It is that with which, in complete spontaneity, she identifies herself most intimately. And as with her beauty, consider also her grace. Think of the adroitness of her fingers. Consider also the dexterity of the performer, the talent of the artist, the virtuosity of the pianist. We can truly say, "Their soul is in their fingers."

The hand cannot be separated from the head, the body from the soul: it is all one.

Such a unity of existence, where one would not have to distinguish between body and "soul," is perfectly expressed by the idea and experience of *grace*, incarnate in the pretty girl and in the harmonious Adonis with his perfectly oiled muscles. And we should consider as a *dis-grace* our perception of the body as an object (either submissive or intractable) distinct from ourselves. We should underline the secondary, artificial, and, to a certain extent, abnormal and pathological nature of such a perception. This segregation of the body comes, let us say, by the nature of things, or, if one likes, by *the Fall* (*sin*), pathology, and death. Adam *does not have* a body; he *is* one.

One of the intentions of this book is to show the parallelism between the divorce of the individual from his body and the divorce of humanity from its corporeality, from the world. For the present I would simply suggest that the communion of an original humanity with the universe (from which it does not yet distinguish itself), and the unity of the sound man with his organism, both proceed from a single anthropological vision.

This original communion, this unity which does not yet involve a *problem*, this consciousness that is not yet a consciousness of self (or *for self*), can be called "predualist." It is predualist because it precedes or is ignorant of the opposition to the world and correlatively, the autopositioning of the self, both of which signify conflict, war, hostility, pride, revolt, and finally the objectification of the world, as such, before the self. I would add that this predualism precedes the "effability" [15] of the world (Ricoeur). The world emerges from pure *appearing* to objectivity, as from dream to speech. The body, as well as the world, will become the prey or the enemy, the target that is aimed at. The body will become the culpable.

It is possible, both in animals and in man, for the struggle for survival to be reconciled with what we call a predualist communion. Nevertheless, this struggle presages and begins the dualist rupture. The subjective partitioning of the indi-

vidual is born from preconscious opposition. The animal continues to struggle, suffer, and die without making a distinction
between his self and his body (without *speaking*), and without distinguishing himself from the world in whose matrix he
evolves somnambulant. The awakening of man to the aggression of the world places him as a subject both distinct from
the world and distinct from his body. The two objectifica-
tions go hand in hand. Objectification means both *rupture* and
engagement of the object. How can this parallelism and this
identity between the opposition to the world and opposition
to the body be illustrated? By the *Fall*, the symbol of a race
placing itself in opposition to Creation, and by *sickness*, the
symbol of the individual in opposition to his own body? This
would be conversely analogous to the parallelism between the
innocence believed to exist originally and health, to the grace
of the soul and the grace of the body. In short, this parallelism
can be summed up in a word: grace. On the level of our living experience, it is important to understand how *sickness* can
constitute the event, the accident that separates us from our
bodies.

My body is identified with me all the better when nothing
grates ("Let it serve me more submissively," says the popu-
lar language, which is always dualist). It ceases to be me from
the time it betrays me. Thus it is no longer the pretty girl: the
deformed woman *has* a body, which she puts up with. It bur-
dens her like a millstone, a stranger, an enemy. The body, in
the view of the sick person who is suffering, is considered as
separate from him: traitor, slave, recalcitrant servant. Abuse
is hurled at it: "You tremble, carcass"; it is bullied.

My body unceasingly reminds me of my finitude, of my
maladroitness: I miss the nail, the screwdriver slips, I slip, fall,
look ridiculous. To the grace of the dancer on ice skates, contrast the inflexibility of the body, the disjointed puppet. The
limits of one's height (the dwarf cannot reach the elevator but-
ton), the limits of one's "best performances," the weakening
that comes with age, the misery of the old person, a whole tra-

dition teaches us that misery comes through our body and its vicissitudes.

Sickness, then, would seem to be the characteristic and description of the body as *separate*. The isolation of those with contagious diseases, leprosariums, the quarantining of plague-infected ships — these are some examples of images furnished by sickness to a *dualism* that segregates us from our own bodies. This analytic dualism that affects us all (men of the streets, patients, physicians, scholars, philosophers) thus finds a permanent source and its justification in the complications of sickness. This is why it has been necessary to build, from the bottom up, an ethic and a spirituality of sickness. Indeed, would such an ethic have any *raison d'être* if dualist segregation had not already quarantined the body, making it the stranger-enemy?

All our technical and ethical attitudes come from this dualist separatism. Philosophies and wisdoms teach us how to subdue the body, as one breaks a wild horse. Medicine teaches us to combat the blunders and failures of this unsatisfactory auxiliary. Man has created parallel systems: ethics, to guard against the existence of evil in this world, and medicine, to guard against sickness.[16] These are two currents that could be rejoined in order to encompass in the same regard a therapeutic of sickness and a spirituality of suffering.

II

This experience of sickness is the source of a dualism that splits the body from the person in order to turn it into an instrument of more or less good quality, a useful object or a nuisance. However, this should be qualified. Sickness operates less schematically. Certain illnesses (in mental patients, the aged, or in nursing infants) do not participate in the autopositioning of the adult. They make no distinction between their person and the situation in which they exist. They are completely involved in a sort of suffering communion, which belongs to the same order as that of the primitive and of the animal in the bosom of Great Mother Earth. Certain illnesses overwhelm the individual, submerging him to the point where he is no longer anything but sickness, and he rediscovers that communion in the Suffering Mother where the I and the Thou are no longer recognized.

Sometimes the individual is so inundated with pain and extreme fatigue that he no longer has the force to resist. No matter how benign it is, there is a part of each affection that invades me and converts me without my knowledge and without my being able to distinguish myself from it. At the same time, however, I oppose myself to its aggression. *Each affection contains, at the same time, both the germ of a dualism that creates my opposition and the germ of a contamination that conquers me.*[17] I will have occasion to come back to this later.

Due to this ambiguity of sickness, one could equally say that sickness is first turned into dualism through the capacity for perspective and autopositioning, rather than sickness being the cause of the dualism. One would underline the role of the constitution of the thing as an object of knowledge, emphasizing the passage from the pure immediate perceptible to the intelligible that is the domain of meaning, word, objectivity, etc. But a question of anteriority is not really involved here: let us say that the deficient, lame, pain-ridden, or sick body contributes to the arising of and even provides the occasion (perhaps temporarily) for this psychological, scientific, philosophical, and religious dualism.

The *product* of the scission, of this divorce, which we have seen is of secondary and abnormal nature (the result of a " catastrophe," of a " fall," a rupture, but also the result of the birth of self-consciousness), is what we will call the *body-object*.

What do we mean by this term? I am not my body; I have a body. It is one thing or another. I look at it; I touch it. I am the spectator of my body. I watch it in the process of acting, of fulfilling its task. Afterward I judge its good and bad steps. The body-object is also rightly called "the-body-for-the-other," precisely because others take, vis-à-vis my body, the same position of spectator and utilizer. It is this body which one scrutinizes, feels, analyzes, heals, amputates, dissects, manipulates. It is this body which one drills as one trains an animal. It is this body-object which, at least in the primary analysis, the physician deals with and cares for.

The psychosociological descriptions of the body-object will not be dealt with here (this can be found elsewhere), even though these descriptions touch upon the area under consideration and could clarify certain points of the physician's objectivist attitude. Rather, I will deal directly with this attitude.

The body-object affords us an extremely convenient point of contact. Its success is evidenced by the great progress made in Western technics (chemotherapy, surgery, etc.). This is a success in the application to the living of methods utilized for matter and for mechanisms, according to the animal-machine theory (whose empirical practice goes back to prehistoric times). The first trephining, the first amputation, deals with the body and detaches from the body a piece that has become foreign. This amputated hand is no longer me; I survive this piece of myself that has been cast away from me and seems to continue to live its "hand existence." [18]

Dualism facilitates the task of the physician and that of the patient. It permits the physician to attack the affected organs, and permits the patient to exorcise their ravages. It is indeed a matter more of an exorcism than of a therapeutic. Dualism allows one to localize and identify the adversary. Every day someone asks me: "Is it my liver, Doctor, or my stomach?" It is handy for us to agree together on the guilty organ or on the infectious agent or the incriminated poison. This is a triumph of the *body-anatomical*, of the *body-surgical*, of the body-object partitioned and classified as organs and pieces, each of which will become the victim and the property of some "specialist." Agreed, many lesional affections readily lend themselves to this parceling,[19] and the patients are benefited by it. In such cases the art of healing progresses. But this parceling extends dangerously into the area of so-called "functional" affections. In these cases the blame is laid on pathological entities that almost seem to be object-idols: heredity, genes, and other corpuscles, antigens. In one's kit there are a whole battery of tests, and the only reason all of them are not tried is because the patient has allergic reactions. Neuroses and psychoses (when one has not given in to the temptation to specify the cause as a lesion, a localization, or a cerebral dysfunction) are offered up in sacrifice in the idolatry of "complexes," "frustrations," and other gods.

It is so true, and we insist on it, that the body-object is, in the final analysis, only the materialization, the solidification of an operation of human understanding, which is objectifying. That is to say, human understanding is not only capable of *recognizing* the "object-ness" of the object, but also is *constitutive* of its objectiveness as such. We objectify in order to analyze and in order to act. Such is our strength and our weakness. It is our strength, in effect, because this power of objectification gives us a control over reality; it is our weakness because this very control removes us from reality and constitutes, finally, an alienation. These are the two foci.

III

We have said that the body-object has brought great practical gains, and, consequently, the body-object contains a great deal of truth in scientific, technical, artistic, ethical, and religious realms. To forget this, in favor of a kind of poetic-metaphysical communion with the universe, would be both puerile and dangerous. For example, the adherents of a medicine concerned with respecting the natural defense reactions of the body are too quick sometimes, in my opinion, to reject chemicotherapeutic and surgical aids. As I said before, certain illnesses lend themselves admirably to the concept of the body-object. This should be taken into account and profited from.

It is sometimes heard that when a case of pneumonia is treated with some type of antibiotic, an easy " gadget " is being substituted for the subject's means of defense, the biological antibodies, the psychological resources. In short, the man is weakened. The antibiotic has only dodged a necessary confrontation and postponed the inevitable. A sickness cannot be cut short, because it manifests a more vast problem of life and generally results in a lesion of the individual's relationship with himself and his environment. It is not a good idea to abort the phases of maturation in an illness; the biopsychological times do not grow shorter or disappear: " It is necessary to wait for the sugar to melt."

My answer to that is that it is only true to a certain degree, for the syncopated rhythms of modern life not only impose a pressure that it would be futile to flee [20] but also and especially call forth vital unforeseen inventions. Our rhythms are not inescapable; life is not ignorant of certain so-called miraculous brusque changes (I am thinking of certain healings that are qualified as being miraculous, without raising the problem of miracles), those unexpected happenings whose defensive reactions are not customary, and which faith, for example, calls into operation. This involves no less the allowing of the " natural " maturation of the time of sickness and convalescence to take its course. The acceleration in this case could be called cultural; it would cut short the duration, the suffering.

In fact, the vital economy of suffering and of sickness does not permit us to be equivocal and to provoke disconcerting interventions. The contemporary acceleration with antibiotics is, to be sure, coupled with a type of psychological and social sluggishness that prolongs convalescence as long as facilities and money allow. This is one of the worst examples of complicity between two forms of progress, both valuable but working in inverse directions. On the contrary, a chemicotherapeutic acceleration which would be joined with a desire to shorten the periods of inaction, to return one sooner to work, would have the beneficial result of avoiding certain asthenias which formerly ended in the waning of illnesses "cured by themselves." In short, although it is good to respect the times of healing and not to permit oneself to be involved in the infernal rhythm of modern life, I hold that it is proper for man to impose his rhythm on the universe. It is advisable to make widespread but discerning use of chemical tools (not at random, as some facile and commercialized forms of medicine do). Such tools accelerate the time span of the illness, helping to restore an interrupted activity and avoiding discouragement (which the sick person does not dare to decide if it is an essential part of the trial or if it is an upsetting accident that turns the trial from its proper direction). Therapeutic approaches always have a double meaning: it is necessary to give them the meaning that will integrate them to the movement, the general ascent of man. And all therapeutic devices, antibiotics and others, can cooperate in promoting such a movement.

To conclude concerning the medical advantages of dualism and of its material utensils (chemistry, surgery, etc.), it cannot be said for certain that they do more harm than good on the level of our personal vocation. It would be useless to place dualism in general in opposition to the unity of our development. Dualism can play the role of the *occasion* and *instrument* of personal totality, if one knows how to understand and use dualism in the proper way.[21]

IV

Such would also be our position, regarding the segregating dualism of the body, in the much broader area embracing and flowing over from medicine into aesthetics and ethics. Dualism does not permit itself to be rejected in Manichaean fashion; it is more correct and more judicious to see it as a *moment* and an *instrument* of our unity, under the very appearance of division.

I believe in the benefits and in the partial truth of the dualism that separates man from his body and from the world, and in the partial truth of the very movement of objectification. The middle or intermediate stage of the "small I" (von Dürckheim), the moment and movement of self-affirmation, of withdrawal, of distance and of opposition to the world, of defiance to all subservience (first a defiance by my own body, then considered as an element of the world in face of the ego or self), all of this contains some truth.

On the one hand, there is the moment of the conflict: insubordination, rebellion, defeat, withdrawal into self, unhappy conscience, flight, resignation, treason, repudiation, and all the rest. We will come back to that later. Now, besides this moment of the conflict, there is also inseparably the moment of conquest and of rightful triumph, the moment of the "best performance" regarding the world and my body.

Dualism marks the setting right of the patient, who "takes the bull by the horns," does not become resigned, and masters and overcomes his illness and his body. To be sure, in this combative setting-right there is a burdensome inflexibility whose dangers are recognized today,[22] but there is also a saving exertion of energy.

It is also instructive to point out the positive aspects of the Herculean symbol, of muscular strength, of intelligence, of dogged labor, and the triumphant aspects of calamity.

The era of mature humanity, which follows the maternal age in the bosom of nourishing nature from which humanity does not yet differentiate itself, is the era of muscular opposition, of force. This is exemplified in our modern civilization by the fight for survival, with its smell of "free enterprise," of merciless competition, and of commercial ugliness. But it is also exemplified by the conquest, mastery, transformation, and possession of the world.

Moreover, it would hardly be exact to restrict this attitude to

Western and antique dualism. The Bible, from the time when man first became aware of God's design (finally recounted in the later book of Genesis), assigns to man the dualist mission of transforming and possessing the earth: " Fill the earth and subdue it; and have dominion over the fish of the sea," etc. (ch. 1:28). As we will see, the Bible contains both an anti-dualism of body and soul and a different dualism, one concerned to demythologize the world in order to set it over against man. Just as there is not always a parallelism between the dualism of the body and the dualism of the world, neither is there always a parallelism between such a dualism (of the body or of the world) and what we could call the segregation of the body or of the world. We will return to this subject later. The Jewish laws of hygiene objectivize the body without separating it into a philosophy of the disincarnated soul.

In any case, the dawning of the autopositioning is not recounted simply as a misfortune (original sin, the violation of the tree of the knowledge of good and evil), but also as a vocation, a mission conferred by the Creator: " You will dominate over the world." This mission, which some have wrongly thought to be repudiated by Christianity, allies closely Greek activism and Jewish activism. In contradistinction to Hindu passivism, the universalism of Occidental *work* furnishes the significant resultant of it: work, civilization, culture, fabricative and inventive intelligence, worker, industrial, and technical intelligence. This is true not only of mechanics and the mechanical spirit, but also in the discipline of the body and hygiene.

Thus the body participates in this architectural objectification of the whole of the universe. Health is tied to aesthetics; struggle and strength are allied with beauty (of a certain type). The body, in its architecture, resembles a temple whose pillars (the sculpture of muscular forms, the development of the thorax, etc.) are characteristic of a Western ethico-aesthetic " school." This school is contrasted with the ethico-aesthetic school of Buddhism, for example, whose graphs and

forms (of visceral polarity) are centered not on the power of
the thorax and its members but on the balance of the stomach
(*hara*). In the language of Bachelard, so useful in contrasts of
this type, Occidental dualism turns toward extraversion, hand
to hand with the world, and gives a favored status to the
organs of relationship that project us inappositely on things
(it involves a control over things). Hindu monism is turned
toward the inner self, toward introversion, the intimity of the
body as the intimity of the cosmos. Intensely concentrated
attention on the organs of nutrition certainly lead quite well
to a type of objectification of the internal organ and is necessary to its mastery (mastery of the intestine, of the heart, etc.).
But this very objectification aims at disappearing in the communion that dissolves the individual in the universe. This is
an ethic-aesthetic of participation, not of opposition.

In any event, I must qualify here what I said in beginning
with the athlete " with well-oiled muscles " as an example of
the predualism of the body. The fine forms and proud strength
have nothing to do with the feeling so well expressed in the
proverb: " To fit neatly into one's skin." The body-subject and
the body-object, here as everywhere, are interwoven. The
athlete (I should rather say the " superathlete "), who is at
one with his body, can nevertheless see his body become the
slave to pain, the docile and difficultly borne slave. This type
of dualism in no way resembles that of the sick person of
whom we will also speak, who is served by a body of sweating
flab rather than the hard sweating of the athlete. These types
of dualism no more resemble each other than either of them
resembles the dualism of the philosopher or of the believer.

This first qualification in our schemas leads to a second:
sickness is far from being the only source of the dualism that
separates us from our bodies. The victorious and technical intellect and muscular extraversion also create dualism. In sum,
the two sources of dualism are conquest and defense. For both
it is necessary to be " at two " with the world, " at two " with
my body.

V

The Stoic attitude furnishes the complex visage of defense and conquest, even while it goes beyond dualism and offers us proof of the absence of a real antinomy between dualism and monism.

First of all, we should point out the utility and truth of a Stoiclike voluntaryism, which knows " to put the body in its place." The " small I " has a certain nobility when it pushes its defiance vis-à-vis the world to the point of impassiveness and stoical indifference. Insensibility cancels out, if it knows to go to the end of its logic, and reaches a loosening up and reconciliation with the body and with the world.

The leg of Epictetus is not Epictetus: it can be handled as one likes. And so for all of that which does not depend on me: possessions, health, comfort, affections, wife and children, my very life. These things surround one in concentric circles, at the center of which " Job-the-divested " rediscovers the dolorous center of *his body*, the ulcers of his body.

All this is true for the Jew as for the Greek, but in what a diametrically opposed style! The body-being becomes a body-having (for the Jew I would more readily say that it is the world of having that comes to be confused with his very being and flesh).

At the limit of dualism the body is only a golden parcel, an idol from which it is necessary to be detached. The *body-temptation*, belonging to certain moral and religious attitudes as well as to a certain pseudo-Christianity, is found then, as a feeble relation, in the encounter of the body-object subjugated by Stoicism. The same contempt is found (as far as contempt resembles pride),[23] it seems, in the Puritan who is ashamed and trembling with his body and in the Roman who abandons his hand to be burned without batting an eye. The two poles of dualism appear again. At first glance, there is no difference between the detestation of the weak and the pride of the strong. At first the dualism of failure has the same look as the dualism of success. For the Puritan (and the Stoic, who resembles him initially) the body is the Tempter, the enemy; sex is included in the area of sin; it is necessary to beat and murder this body in order to escape the traps of its gluttony and lust. What violence and what courage! Yet it is a pseudo-courage and a cowardly violence. The superficial appearances mask the discordant reality of a dualism of failure characterized by resentment and of a dualism of success characterized by universal participation, *where it is no longer recognized as a dualism*. The dualism of the weak ends in a definitive and irremediable divorce; the dualism of the strong falls as a ripe fruit in the postdualism of the reconciliation with the world. The Stoic, who prescribes detachment from the healthy or sick body, rejoins at the end of his logic, *when he succeeds*, the communion with the individual and universal body, in a pantheistic monism that relates it to the plan of Being.

In modern language, the body-object is called our "facticity," that is, an ensemble of determinisms and conditionings: temperament and character, my temper through my temperament, etc., on which our freedom is moored, as a trading in to my account of this very facticity. *All the modern antidualist approaches of existential inspiration are no less rooted in a language and an experience that are dualist.*

No facial muscle trembles, at "H hour," in a man *of character*. On the contrary, it is the body that betrays the emotion. It sometimes happens that the man condemned to death, even the intrepid man, becomes weak in the knees, his sphincters relax, and he feels his body give way under him. Either he detests or he pities this deceitful support that has failed him at the crucial moment. He has fear and he pities his body. If I were to ask him, "*Are you* your body?" he would give a denial in every sense of the word. No one could be more dualist than he is. And the same is true for the sick person. He does not want to be identified with his legs, which it is necessary to change the position of, nor with his stomach, which soils him, nor, indeed, of this whole carcass, which is in the charge of others and of himself.

Modern education, as well as that of ancient times, seeks to master the body. It must be bridled as a restive mount. We give little esteem to the emotional person who is "beside himself," delivered over to his body and his surroundings; we penetrate him as one penetrates a poorly guarded fortress, through his weak points and his failures.

These examples are given in order to show that the body-object gives rise not only to our technical exploits but also to our asceticisms and our ethical thought. It should not be forgotten that *our very manner of combating dualism speaks its language.*

But I could not leave the subject of the body-object without speaking of *its* death. It seems that the attitude in the face of death expresses the unanimity of all dualist idealisms, from the Platonic to the pseudo-Christian. The death that we encounter at each step (sickness at its point of rupture, the critical test of our common life with our body, i.e., the test of our corporeality) — does it not deliver us from this perishable and decaying covering? And does not the soul survive in the "beyond," escaped from the body-prison, the transparent soul finally to itself, immortal and blessed? The theme of the *immortality of the soul* fosters all the spiritualist equivocations. Under a rubric that we think to be traditional, it mingles pagan and philosophic idealisms of the body-object together with the religious spiritualism of Judeo-Christian inspiration. We would do better to call this latter, in accordance with the Creed, a resurrection of the body-subject, that is, of the man.

From this summary inquiry, we should, nonetheless, retain the value and truth of the body-object in the heart of a noble ethic of defense and of victorious self-recovery, of steadfastness and of balanced temperament — whatever happens to the body, be it prison, sickness, or death. The particular freedom that characterizes such a dualism should rather be called *emancipation* than fulfillment (or accession).

CHAPTER II

The Body-Object: Summons and Snare
for the Physician

I

THE *objectification* OF OUR BODY IS INDISPENSABLE FOR SCIENCE, and especially for medicine; it is a constant in our attitudinal responses in life, sickness, and death. Yet in the final analysis the objectification is only a convention of the technical and the ethical understanding. It is a method, and if one is not careful it can become a vice of theoretical thought and of practical action, which will falsify reality and our lives. Thus it is necessary to point out its dangers.

The services rendered by the concept of the " body-object " are inestimable, on the condition that we do not mistake this *product* of our analysis for reality itself. It is customary to dissect the cadaver in order to learn anatomy, but the cadaver bears only a crude resemblance to the live being. The " body-object " is a dead body.

It is significant that in French one speaks of the " chemical body," while one also uses " body " to refer to one's *living* body. Both " bodies " undoubtedly compose " structures," and we no longer assume that it is simply a matter of adding certain external elements to others. But the *unity* of a living body asserts itself through its internal regulations, its embryological growth, and its maturation. It behaves as an *individual*. We will see later in what conditions it behaves as a person.

I have already mentioned the first consequence of this *unity* of the living body (cf. Introduction). Sickness is not "some part" in the individual. It is situated neither in a particular organ nor in a particular function. It is an example of the mobilization and reorganization of the whole individual. The *objective* view facilitates the circumscription of the illness by the physician and by the patient. We measure insufficiencies and excesses through the use of "physiological" statistics (blood pressure, blood tests, etc.). "Normal" aspects serve as reference points to evaluate abnormal states, both lesional and functional, in a given area.[24]

This is an approximation both invaluable and specious. Illness is not simply a matter of certain homogeneous quantitative variations, no more than it affects only a fragment of the living being. It modifies the totality of the structure into a new totality, in no way homogeneous with the former one.

On first glance, it would seem proper to grant that the anomaly magnifies normal phenomena, like a microscope (the illness becoming a better field of study for the physiologist). But in reality, the magnification is only a myopic way of considering what is in fact a *qualitative* change. As Bergson remarked in his analysis of effort, it involves an analogous language projecting *qualitatively heterogeneous* phenomena into the homogeneous space of quantity. We speak of variations in terms of *hypo* and *hyper*, of quantitative homogeneity, of lesional localizations, through an abstraction that isolates a function or an organ. Such *evidences* or *points of reference* are easier to follow in diagnosis. Indeed, blood pressure, blood tests, and the like are only points of reference useful in detecting and watching an illness (which, in reality, changes the entire individual). Let us not confuse a visible and easily measured *effect* (but not always the most important, such as cholesterol in the lipides) with its cause, which integrates it into a global transformation having a meaning. Illness is a true human conduct; functioning as a whole, the organism assumes a healing posture. It begins to adjust to the aggression and to the functional possibilities (such possibilities are more limited perhaps, but they are nonetheless original).

Thus we see in illness a positive contrivance affecting the entire man. A new structure is designed with a view to confronting *in another way* the struggle for survival. It is privation, but it is also invention, an original and personal synthesis, differing from the former state in nature rather than in degree, in quality as well as in quantity.

This disorder is a new order; this non-sense has a sense. As the philosophers say, regarding an emotion or a faint, it is "intentional." Like an emotion or a faint, sickness is a *conduct*.

Certain qualifications should be made at this point, namely, that pathological behavior does not have a *meaning* in the same way that healthy behavior does: impotent and disoriented, the patient often becomes the prey of his own past, of his automatisms, of his environment. And one speaks quite rightly of *disintegration* in sickness, of *integration* of all functions in the "normal" state, and of *reintegration* in healing. However, in saying that the broken sense of sickness is still a sense, I mean that it proceeds from an oriented intention that affects not only certain organs or cells but also the entire individual (whether or not he is aware of it) with his hormones, his brain, his character, his convictions, his environment. In such a perspective, nonmeaning is still a form of meaning. As Paul Ricoeur has written: "Nonsense or senselessness is still in the dimension of sense. The hermeneutic of sense always moves from the least significant sense to the most significant sense. Psychotherapists [one could say "physicians in general"] want only to bring about the acceptance of a new sense that would be lived on a more authentic level and that would manifest the intentional reality of life in a more veracious way." [25]

Thus my sick body expresses me entirely as *subject:* it is a *body-subject.* In asserting that sickness (as health and healing) organizes the individual in a new attitude of defense and readjustment that constitutes a true biological, mental, and social *conduct*, I mean that my body responds not only to a local aggression, but to a general situation, to a total conflict. My sick body is inseparable from my consciousness as a civilized man in society. My overtures and my responses to the world are already brought into play *immediately* through my body, without necessarily appealing to my clear, pondered, verbal, official, and advertised understanding.[26]

Indeed, the latter, on the contrary, would conceal, by means of my so-called *public* behavior, a deeper and more secret conflict. My public behavior is only a partial and selective manifestation of this conflict. As is well known, the discoveries of Freud and the searchings of psychoanalysis have thus unearthed this profoundly corporeal " depth psychology." One speaks, for example, of guilt or of failure conduct, intentional conducts that are played out on the stage of the body — no one would say that such a drama is a drama of the soul! [27]

All of this is well known; I mention it only to support my critique of the body-object, built of bits and pieces somewhat like a self-propelling mechanism. A patient comes to me for consultation. His painful organ is not always the real seat of his illness. It is rather like the spokesman of it, the herald, or the hawker, similar to those mourners who make a profession of wailing to announce a bereavement. Thus, in Balint's excellent phrase,[28] the sick person " makes an overture " to his physician and to those around him. The sick organ is the instrument of appeal without its being aware of it: this organ translates for us, in coded language (" colitis," " gastritis," " a migraine "), a painful problem of life which is hidden more deeply and which the person was unaware of, not " wanting " to become aware of it in order to confront it as such.

Such an " overture " has many meanings. First of all, it has the signification of an obscure pretext for attracting attention to oneself, to beg for help, for the affection one feels deprived of. It is a sign, a poorly formulated appeal. We often see this appeal raised in a neglected wife whose husband thinks only of his business affairs. He alternates indifferently between his newspaper and his telephone. She falls ill, complaining of discomforts that never let up, indeed, that start afresh elsewhere. "He doesn't want to understand that I'm sick; he doesn't pay any attention to me." The more she whines, the more her irritated husband turns his head and absents himself from this conjugal hell, thus perpetuating the vicious circle created by a pressing but poorly understood message.

The message is so poorly expressed that the physician himself, if he is not alert, attentive, formed by a medicine completely different from that of organic investigations, will not understand its true meaning either. Being in turn led astray, he will respond in the wrong manner or at the wrong time, whether it be in bluntly refusing the patient's hand held out to him ("Your tests, your X-rays, everything is negative; there's nothing wrong with you; it's your nerves.") or in accepting, on the contrary, the "overture" of the patient *as such*. He falls thus into the trap of this "liver ailment" or "stomach ailment" which the patient had unknowingly and quite innocently set up before the world around him. The physician scents the trap, but *it would be too long and too difficult for him to wage the war*. So he resigns himself, in complete awareness of the cause, to the easy solution, which consists of diagnosing and treating the apparent illness.

I said that the "overture" of the patient had several meanings. The organ "overtured" (which can be, moreover, that of a spouse, of a son or daughter, victims offered to the physician by the neurosis of the parents) also constitutes a refuge against personal difficulties, a conduct of defense for eluding a problem while at the same time giving it a solution. This is a show that we should not knock down without precautions, yet it is nevertheless a vicious show, since it creates and installs a pseudo-organic affection to which we will contribute, which we will reinforce through our inopportune objective organicist attitude (bioradiological tests, hospitalizations, specialists, chemical drugs, etc.). "The patient, being unable to find a solution, takes refuge in sickness. If one of his overtures is accepted by the physician, there is a danger that all the patient's energies will be monopolized in the fight of the accepted illness." (Balint.)

In short, the snare that we must avoid is that of accepting as such the objective sickness that is proposed to us. This is the snare of the body-object, *in forgetting that the discomfort proposed by the patient is an illness of the body-subject*. This discomfort is the visible face of an invisible problem. This problem cannot be vaguely guessed at. It is necessary to learn how to bring the problem to light, to decipher it and bring the patient to an understanding of it. This is a level of diagnosis and treatment that goes beyond the body-object (the collection of organs and functions) in order to arrive at the concrete reality of the body-subject. This requires not only a long acquaintanceship with the patient and his family (an inestimable advantage of the general practitioner over the specialist), but above all a conversion of our way of looking at illness, a change of attitude, finally, a long apprenticeship, a technique that one learns, that cannot be improvised. The failure of our medical education on this point cannot be deplored too much.[29]

II

What is, indeed, our ordinary attitude in the face of illnesses of the body? As I previously pointed out, the patient is spontaneously preoccupied with his internal organs: "Is it my liver, Doctor?"[30] To this inquiry we give assent through some type of label that is just as puerilely localizing, as well as through the prescribing of cholagogues and antispasmodic chemicals. One would justify this, if forced to, when the absence of a precise lesional localization (let us not overlook the fact that this is the case most of the time in current practice) leaves the field open to any localization, to any description no matter how fanciful, as long as it is conceivable. Who would deny the incalculable number of patients treated throughout

life for " the liver," or for " colitis," when the sole proof for the
condition is furnished by the finger of the patient and the painful palpation here and there of the physician. Volumes could
be written on the fortunes of "painful points."

But I am also speaking of the discomforts that the arro-
gance of an endoscopy or a radiography circumscribe in some
nook of our anatomy: bronchial catarrh, stomach ulcers,
hemorrhagic rectocolitis, etc. These are manifest and visible:
do we not have the right to set out a precise therapeutic,
proper to the affected region, codified by the authority of
teachers and scientific publication?

Well, although the error of this approach is not immediately
obvious when the illness manifests an objective lesion, the
tragedies from it are no less real. For example, the excision of
a calculous vesicle rendered responsible for migraines and
cases of heartburn leaves the unfortunate woman suffering
just as much, if not more. Was not the lesion evident? But the
fact is that a lesion or anomaly, no matter how precise it might
be, is not necessarily illness. The excision of the anomaly, let
me make myself clear, does not lead to healing in these conditions.[31]

How many people with authentic stomach ulcers are left
mutilated after the gastrectomy, because there had been a
failure to take account of the context, not only *biological*
(neurohepatic subjects, humoral unstables in the precarious
proteinic balance, etc.) but also *psychological* (anxiety, professional difficulties, family problems, etc.). We have forgotten
the person and have seen only the organ. We have forgotten
the body-subject and have fallen into the snare of the body-
object, of the anatomical body, of the surgical body!

The false trail of organicism is caught in the very act of
therapeutic and surgical inexpediencies in the so-called functional illnesses, where functional anomalies are observed without anatomical lesions. The physician of the body-object
persists then in treating the whole in the part: functional
surgery thus claims to treat the whole terrain on the stage of

the organ. For example, in "biliary dystonies" the surgeon attempts to obtain mitigation through a local operation; however, the trouble is still elsewhere, and indeed throughout. The failures are numerous of a therapeutic of cutting up.[32] However, there are also some successes, for the part is also a summary of the totality of the body. It is indirectly this totality that one affects in each of the parts. An exploratory laparotomy is sometimes beneficent in a functional illness, but it would be risky to count on it.

I would add that our very manner of practicing medicine, by the individual action or on the particular organ or function affected, contributes to the parceling of the patient. We treat an attack, an organ, a lesion, a symptom, neglecting the person in his depth and continuity, his environment and his problems of life.

The economic organization and the specialistic and competitive anarchy of medicine follow the same course as the objectivist and materialist conception of the body. And, to the detriment of the patients, they are interrelated and even render mutual service.

How do things operate in our present organization?[33] Each patient goes freely to consult the physician of his choice (which is to say, on the basis of public opinion, on the advice of a neighbor, or, ironically, on the basis of a localizing diagnosis that the patient himself has preliminarily formulated: "I am suffering from my liver, I'm going to see a liver specialist, I want some X-rays of my liver, I want treatment for my liver"). There is no need of going to the local physician. That would only be a waste of money! The patient, who has already chosen his orientation, goes directly to the specialist. Thus he comes, obtains the treatment he expected, pays, leaves, free to return or not, to follow his treatment or not, to change his physician at will, according to the immediate success or lack of success of the first drugs. This is piecemeal medicine. The patients are spontaneously organicist. They are concerned with the body-object. Why then should we bother, since the body-object is also *our* concern?

The patients have enough scientific understanding only to transform their bodies into mysterious and subtle mechanisms, somewhat like a television set. The illness fares well to overcome the patient completely, and although he is vaguely aware of it, he is entirely in agreement with the localizing parceling out which exorcises his suffering and appeases his anxiety. He knows what he has, " whence it comes "! Moreover, he expects the physician to respond to the need that he expresses in the very terms that he gives: " My liver, my stomach, my spinal cord."

Failing to obey this imperious solicitation, the physician stands to put off, rebuff, or lose his patient by telling him that his liver is of little consequence in the illness, that, rather, he must accept some old frustration or overcome some fear. The patient will " autoselect," in Balint's phrase, some more " understanding " colleague. It is thus that the pathology of free choice makes us slaves of the mentality of the public, against its own interest. We are prisoners, at one and the same time, of modern technocratic organicism and of a pseudo " liberal " system that has given birth to this spoiled child — " the consumer king." This latter makes the law (whether we want to help or simply to earn our living), but the expense is great.

It is not that the organicist compromise based on the body-object does not have its short-term advantages of facility. It brings momentary satisfaction to the physician, and above all, to the patient. It shows that the patient was right, and furthermore, it gives him a *reason for living*. He becomes preoccupied with treating his *chronic* " colitis," which each augur, consulted in his turn, and each pharmaceutical speciality (of which each day brings new, and for every taste) treats partially and provisionally. Since " it is chronic," why should anyone wonder that it is not healed? Everybody is content. Social security [34] is there to take care of the expenses of the body-object, *and of the body-object only*.[35] But to the body-object nothing is refused. Examinations are repeated how many times for no reason. The patient is sent several times to specialists and to the hospital. He is observed and carefully examined through tests and dosages. "We can find nothing wrong with you; you can go home."

Meanwhile, social security pays for the pharmaceutical specialities that overcrowd the cupboards (or the refrigerator; I have seen one devoted solely to such specialities, rather than to foodstuffs).

As for the physician, does he not earn his living thanks to the manipulations of the body-object? He does "all that is in his power" to eliminate a cancer or some other specter. He is appreciated and *successful*, for he satisfies his clientele. Has he not without batting an eyelid asked a specialist and obtained reports as negative as they are reassuring? One has done everything. Prescriptions have been given. Everything turns out fine, although it has been costly. And each continues to suffer, the patient and, sometimes, the physician.

We now come to the related problem of specialization. The excesses of this have already been denounced, both by myself and others.[36] Our age (and are not our patients affected by the mentality of the age?) is tremendously prone to overvalue technical procedures and stainless steel apparatuses.[37] Moreover, in the system of medical practice such as we have in Europe and America, where the price is fixed according to the individual treatment (action), the technical act devoted to the body-object is worth ten times more than the prolonged discussion (in which there is nothing to do, but in which the body-subject manages its healing). (Such prolonged discussions are, moreover, difficult, strewn with snares, risking, through transfer and countertransfer, the putting into opposition of the physician and the patient.)

In such a system, how can we expect the physician not to yield to the seductions of the body-object, which profits him more and brings him less worries? This is what I mean when I say that the economic system and organicist technolatry go hand in hand. I belabor this convergence not only to put it on trial with an end of practical reform, but also to bring to light *the anthropological presuppositions of our medicine based on the body-object.* Everything is tied together: commerce and competition, pharmacy, medical education, the mentality of patients, the system of payment, nosology, symptomatic or organic medicine, the biochemical or mechanical body-object.

The image of the specialist provides an extreme caricature of the *objective* attitude regarding the body: the inhuman specialist, a type of future robot, who depersonalizes patients only because he himself is already depersonalized. In him the scientific objectivity and precision leave nothing to be desired. But the objectivity is illusory and misleads the precision whose features are distorted by too narrow a vision. It is a metamorphosis of the lie, under the good conscience of an impeccable exactitude. It is indeed a matter of mutilating the truth, in the name of truth itself and by a servant of the truth, for truth, as it concerns us, is sick persons, men and women living and suffering in a social milieu. The specialist deprives an electric current of its mystery: what pride there is in being invincible in such technical exploits. " I don't pay any attention to anything outside my domain; that is not my business." " Your illness has nothing to do with your heart." " The gynecological examination is negative; I'm sending you back your patient." " Gastroduodenal X-ray negative; rachidian bulb suspect." Are such incomplete practitioners of medicine still physicians? They are certainly precise technicians. But in my opinion there is no medicine worthy of the name without a total critical thought, without an attentive comprehension of man.[38]

There is a deadly conspiracy that weaves a corselet around the specialist, making him invulnerable in his position but extremely vulnerable in his movements. This armor-plating is imposed on him by the diversification of techniques. In order to master an operation, he must repeat it a thousand times. He does not have time to be concerned with things beyond his attention. His colleagues expressly ask of him only one thing, and they would be upset were he to go beyond his specialty. They are filled with admiration for his competence even to the point of overlooking the situation when this competence ends in results that deviate far too widely for one knowing the patient in depth.

The danger is serious and seems to inundate the efforts that are made to oppose the parceling out of medicine, a parceling out that will turn us into specialized laborers. The complexity and interrelatedness of new discoveries work against us. This accumulative effect weighs down on us in all areas of technics and administration (machinism and bureaucracy), to the breaking point where a blunt simplification will come to us perhaps from a self-administration of things. It will be an era of robots.

For the time being, as specialists, daily more numerous and more diverse, we should forget about being physicians in order to try awkwardly to perform the functions of "sub-robot" technicians. It is so true that examinations can often be confided to the nonphysicians. They are already in the highly efficient hospitals, where it is no longer the radiologist who is in charge of X-rays, but a nurse, where it is no longer the gastroenterologist who "tubes" his biliary cases but the nurse who has been trained to perform this daily task. In the fashionable sections of the downtown areas, adorned with the fine name of "specialists," we become benighted artisans of archaic backwardness, as if the new discoveries themselves pushed us back into the horse-and-buggy era.

It pains me to hear radiologists deal with their photographs. Hurry and routine have reduced them to the craft of photography. Also responsible for this is the irrational mode of collaboration with their correspondents, who order films of such and such an organ often without even justifying the films with a clinical explanation (nor do they keep the radiologist informed concerning the later developments of the case). Not knowing what happens to the patients, not having any opportunity of collating their diagnostic technique with the one-shot patients' *bodily* future, they are, in effect, scarcely more advanced than the piecework laborer.

The patient suffers even more from this parceling out. He justifiably complains of no longer having dealings with physicians but with interchangeable white coats who no longer know him and whom he no longer recognizes. These white coats send him from one to the other: "This is no longer my department." Certain failures are produced in the machine, for which the patient bears the expense. For example, he suffers from a stomach disturbance. His physician sends him to the radiology lab. The radiologist writes judiciously and guilelessly: "suspicion of ulcer." Nothing more is asked. From the physician to the specialist, from the specialist to the surgeon, and the possible ulcer can become "ulcer to operate on." There is a lack of human liaison. The patient clamors even louder for a "radical" solution, even when some such cases involve neuropathic disturbances (and the operation will certainly aggravate them). On opening up the patient, no ulcer is found. There is great confusion. Sometimes it happens that an ulcer, between two crises, will escape the eye and the finger of the best surgeon. Is it an ulcer that will reappear tomorrow, or an ulcer that never existed? Does one purely and simply close the wall? Will one mutilate the stomach? These are two difficult choices, which would not have had to be made had one not assumed the liaison and the synthesis, the total responsibility for the entire series of operations. If the wall is reclosed, the patient risks suffering from a real ulcer; if the stomach is operated on, there is a possibility that it will be a nonulcerous stomach. The patient will be greatly bothered by it throughout his life. This is a typical example, happily not too frequent, of the inconveniences resulting from the parceling out of the medicine of the body-object.

A figure, meaningful in one ensemble, is no longer meaningful in a given other ensemble. For example, high blood pressure does not have the same meaning in the description of an acute case of nephritis that it does in a chronic illness. The place of a word in a sentence modifies its meaning; the same is true of an objective given. The context, that is, what I learn and understand of the whole patient, corrects the abstract givens of statistics or films.

How do we guard against the danger of technical abstraction, which ruins the specialist's precious *objectivity* itself and paradoxically transforms the most objective examination into the pure and simple subjectivity of a reading of contrasted shadows? Such a battle against the dangerous neosubjectivity of *the specialists of the body-object* cannot be carried on effectively by isolated individuals. What is necessary is a collaboration, an exchange, incessant dialogue between physicians, so that there can be constituted collegially a consensus of understanding and initiative more vast and more precise than is possible to even the most strenuous efforts of isolated understandings. We also await the day when robots will take our place in performing purely objective tasks that now occupy our time. The day when all information concerning the *object* will be furnished automatically by the robot of service, medicine will become once again what it is: the application of both a total science and a heart to a total man who thinks and who suffers.

III

I have wanted to illustrate here the remarkable convergence of a certain conception of the body and of certain modes of practicing medicine: *the complicity of conceptions and of institutions.*

Modern medicine, proudly surrounded by stainless steel precision apparatuses, symbolizes wonderfully the designs of the body-object, with its promises and its dangers.

The claims of the body-subject, of the unity of the person, and of total medicine, on the contrary, appear archaic and suspect. In the eyes of the orthodox, such claims are in direct line with "faith-healing" and even charlatanry. They are clothed in the finery of alchemy, related to nebulous, humoral, and moral systems of medicine, to concepts of purity and impurity, involving some form of "black magic" or of a medical form of the "power of positive thinking."

This is a strange situation in which the "prospective" attitude (as it is called today), in reality turned toward the syntheses of the future, should be seen as a return to the past. It is also odd to encounter unexpected allies in the clichés brought forth by retrograde physicians (dealing with "trust," "conscience," etc.).

In an article dealing with this question,[39] I traced a parallel between the two equally legitimate needs of medicine and of our patients: the technoeconomic need and the human need. There is also a parallel between these two needs and the two visions of the sickness, which are exactly those of the body-object and the body-subject. "Organic illnesses and functional illnesses are less two types of illness than two ways of fighting against illness. Or better yet, they are two ways of viewing *the* illness, two possible perspectives on the sick man, two fashions of understanding one and the same reality. The one is organicist, localizing and materializing the suffering; the other is structuralist and functional, trying to grasp man in his totality and in his comportment. Thus they are two *methods*. To each a part of reality comes to bring some type of confirmation. Certain illnesses, certain patients, and certain physicians are better adapted to a medicine of the body-object. Others find the medicine of the total body better. These are two methods and two temptations, which would, indeed, produce two camps of physicians and also furnish arguments for or against the traditional, private practice of medicine or the socialist health teams of which some dream for tomorrow." Yet I concluded that this opposition was, in reality, arbitrary; the alliance of free enterprise with personal medicine, and the alliance of socialistic planning with the medicine of the object is in no way inevitable. At most, this schema of alliances can be used as evidence of collusion (on both sides), a collusion that is quite capable of annulling the tendency en-

deavoring to integrate the personal relationship into our tech-
nico-objective needs. Here is where we find again the necessity of a psychotherapeutic education of the general practitioner. We will see later what the exact relations are between
such an education and the meaning of the body-subject. These
relations are closer than we think. As an example, I would
point only to the analysis of transference and countertransference, that is, of the therapeutic relationship as therapy in
psychoanalysis and related or adapted techniques. These lead
to a veritable autocriticism of the physician, to a "purification" of his own attitudes (in the analytical and ethical senses
of the term) in the degree to which he learns to "prescribe
himself" (Balint), a prescription that is an incessant transformation of persons by interaction.

The traditional family physician, through his concrete feeling for the human, refuses (or refused) instinctively to accept
the fiction of the body-object with which specialists and modern techniques are exclusively occupied. He knows (knew)
that the anonymous drug constitutes a scientific error as well as
a harmful action. Operating according to his rough notions
of the influence of the mental on the physical and through a
mature sympathy and a prolonged acquaintance with the patient and his family, the "family" physician acts (acted) on
the whole person while at the same time administering his
pharmaceutical speciality to the body-object.

This old attitude of the general practitioner, which he adopts
instinctively when he enters into dialogue with his patients
and attempts to delve more deeply into their problems, can
serve as a pretext for a reactionary medicine that is the enemy
of technical and social progress. It can hide a "capitalistic"
medicine that serves particular interests, an immobility linked
to outdated pseudoprinciples, covering old privileges and old
ignorances. Ignorance, obviously, should not be confused with
knowledge of the person.

But this same attitude can serve a new medicine that turns
its "prospective" regard toward the future, through and be-

yond objective techniques. In opposition to an antidualism that would like to return to the past, to a mummified and folkloric *predualism*, we call for a *postdualism* (psychosomatic medicine, Neohippocratism, Medicine of the Person) in which we must believe and do everything to participate in. The purpose of this present study is to contribute to the elucidation of this postdualism.

The postdualist aim of the medicine of the future is found, in fact, in a remarkable point of convergence of all contemporary thought, scientific, philosophic, and religious. Modern philosophies fight against the dualisms and the analytical empiricisms or idealisms of the past. Form and Gestalt psychologies, structuralisms, and existentialisms put the accent on human interrelationships and the idea of totality. In the meantime, Christianity is endeavoring to revive the true meaning of the *incarnation* and of the historical and cosmic universality of God's plan.

We intend to place ourselves at the confluence of these currents whose meeting seems so striking to us. A study concerning the *body*, whether such a study comes from the physician, from the patient, from the philosopher, or the Christian, or the Muslim, or the nonbeliever, cannot avoid coming into contact with the other currents that end at the same body-subject, that is, at the body-person. Whatever be the point of departure, whatever be the situation or the discipline that directs one toward the meaning of the body, one is inevitably led toward a synthetic viewpoint that ceases to be exclusively medical, or philosophic, or religious, but is rather all of these at one and the same time. One arrives at the central point where, to want to turn one's back on philosophic reflection and on religious faith, would refalsify scientifically concrete reality. A segregation of philosophic reflection or of religious faith would be a mutilation of our integral approach to the body, whether I am a practitioner or a simple patient confronted with illness and besieged by it. Thus no direction and no dimension will be ignored in the following chapters.

CHAPTER III

The Body-Subject: Structural Totality

I

IN SOME PARTICULARLY SUGGESTIVE PAGES, GABRIEL MARCEL HAS attempted to express the inexpressible relationship of the subject to his body.[40] I do not *have* a body as one disposes of an instrument; and, in one sense, it must be said that *I am my body*, although in another sense I cannot completely identify myself with it. The objectifying attitude, which scrutinizes my body as a spectator and discourses about it,[41] which handles my body as a utensil, is worse than a simple failure of fulfillment or an error of perspective. It is more like a treason or a repudiation. In other words, the error approaches moral error.

Let us point out, before proceeding farther, that in an analysis of this type there is a complicity of ascertainment and need, from the points of view of both ethics and the neutral reflexive description. For the abstract and didactic mind, this is a "mixing of levels." In my meaning, this mixing gives evidence, on the contrary, of a respect for the concrete which, in fact, does not separate the ascertainment from the need. An ascertainment, whatever it might be, is oriented. As response to an implicit question, this ascertainment itself depends on the way in which I have posed the question. A simple error of perspective, if we avoid abstracting it from its situation, if we

leave it " in situation," is always " impure," that is, it is related
to a fault of life. In theory, it is easy to distinguish between
error and fault. An error does not implicate me morally; fault
engages more completely my responsible person. However, in
practice, in the *praxis* and the very depth of existence, responsibility and nonresponsibility are inextricably mixed, which
brings about a confusion of ideas. This is what certain ideas of
political nature have not taken into account, to the great con-
sternation of the " good intention " casuist.[42]

Such a digression is far from being useless, concerning as it
does all along the way our method and our language. Both
approach step by step, in the manner of Gabriel Marcel, ethical thought and descriptive thought, in an integral phenomenology. Yes, the vision of the body-object is both a failure of
fulfillment *and* a repudiation. It would doubtless be easy to
avoid the excesses and abuses of such a method. No criterion,
in fact, blocks it from the route leading to the processes of acts
and of intentions. The temptation is great to question anyone
with the least divergence of opinion: " He does not want to
understand." And in consequence, he is treated severely.[43] The
global method contains the germ of all fanaticisms; the spirit
of " objectivity " at least guarantees tolerance and freedom of
opinion. The rationalist has a field day in denouncing the con-
fusions and the violences of a *pre*positivism which has not yet
arrived at the serene neutrality of the ascertainment (the
ascertainment that forbids itself to judge, that is capable of unlimited understanding).

I subscribe entirely to these criticisms. It also seems to me to
be essential to permit oneself a gathering together of the two
languages (of ascertainment and of need) *only after having
made a distinction between them,* after having passed through
the salutary trial, through the scourging of rational and objective thought. This is a type of initially indispensable introductory examination which could not be dodged. But it would be
injurious to remain at that point, at the sterile and sterilizing
level of analytical objectivity, like a physician who confines

himself to the precise anatomy of the cadaver.

Thus it is necessary to go beyond the distinction between the ascertainment and the need. It is then that the tone of accusation gives way to the tone of prophetic denunciation.[44] Here again, a postdualism of ascertainment-need does not bear any resemblance to the mythical, affective, and primitive predualism (which accuses and exonerates itself),[45] except for an unwarned observer.

II

Let us now turn to the analyses of the body-subject, which are found frequently in the works of contemporary psychologists and philosophers.[46] Our purpose will be to elucidate not only the usual influence of the psychical on the physical and vice versa, but also the *psycho-organic structural unity* (this combined term in no way prejudges the prerogative of the psychic or of the organic), this unity which we call the body, realized in our existence, our behavior, our perceptions, in short, in all that which expresses us, the movements of understanding or of demonstrating.

As everyone knows, our body is not a simple juxtapositioning of homogeneous elements in a homogeneous space. Rather, it is an organization which is located in a space that is oriented according to certain coordinates which are lived before they are objectified. The body is a structured totality in a lived space (J. Wahl).

This means, for one thing, that there is a solidarity among the parts of this unity, that "cordial relationships" and a "government" obtain among these parts ("the head and its members," as the myth expresses it). Even more, there is an intimate union in "one sole flesh" ("This is bone of my bones and flesh of my flesh").

However, the deeper meaning here is that we find ourselves in the presence of the inexpressible unity of life in one person, which analysis tries inadequately to express through descriptions of the *body image,*[47] of the idea of *perception,* and of the idea of *expression.*

It is certain that from the initial embryonic stage the body is potentially oriented and finalized in such a way that the regions are differentiated functionally from each other, each passing from a phase of undifferentiation to an irreversible phase of determination (the cephalic region leading to the posterior regions, etc.). In the embryo as in the adult, there is nonsymmetric high and low, a right and a left. The different parts of the body " are acquainted " with both; we have in us the " image " of our lived body, our " body image," in such an unconscious and implicit way that this image underlying all our movements appears only in its deficiencies.

We speak here of the body image only in order to illustrate the unity of a body-subject. The body image is not only the practical knowledge, the " image " or rather the motor diagram of the differentiated unity and of the reciprocal position of the various regions of the body (high and low, etc.); it is also the practical knowledge, the " image " of these different regions in relation to the surrounding environment, itself oriented and significant. As with the instinctive orientation of birds in space, so does the coordination of our sensations and movements constitute one integral posture, as Goldstein says, of the entire individual with the world. It is from this posture that analysis will abstract a given component, a visual or auditory sensation, equilibrium functions, etc.

In reality, the two knowledges of the body (in relation to its own regions and in relation to the world) are one: it is the same thing to situate myself in relation to myself and to situate myself in the world. A hemiplegic possesses an altered " image " (motor) of his body: a portion of his body becomes a stranger to him, and he no longer connects this arm or this leg either with the rest of his body or with the world. One sees thus partial destructions of the body image through vascular encephalic lesions: a parietal lesion provokes a loss of consciousness for half of the body (a hemi-asomatognosis), which then becomes, for the sick person, an object unduly loaded onto his person. This can lead to a true persecution complex: "What does this piece of flesh want of me?" The illusion of amputees furnishes another example of the permanence of this symbolic "me" that governs our feelings and our behavior.

At two years, the infant will still attempt to feed his foot. Child psychologists underline the central role played by affective messages and their deficiencies in the correct constitution of the body image and of the mental environment up to age ten. This period allows, in short, for the integration of any temporal or spatial event into the unity of the self, lacking which it would remain foreign. Schizophrenia shows us the attack on the integrity, cohesion, and permanence of the body image, which is indissociable from the surrounding environment. The alienated person has lost the "practical image" of his body. Out of this surge all the fantastic images of his delirium: inorganic and other metamorphoses, petrification, and death. "There are no longer organs, sex, or brain; he is another (split personality), and the world no longer exists." The nonsensical ideas of nothingness and immortality, of enclosing the universe, etc., are evidence of a loss both of proportions and of intrinsic and extrinsic relationships.

Merleau-Ponty, utilizing the abundant observational data of Goldstein, has beautifully described this type of innate consciousness by which the body manifests immediate presence as "being-in-the-world," a "perspective-on-the-world." [48] Following Merleau-Ponty, let us take the example of the simple movement of *grasping:* "From the outset the grasping movement is magically at its completion. . . . In this movement the reference is not to the object represented; rather, it is referring to that thing in which we are *in anticipation,* the thing which we pursue. . . . It is the body which 'catches' (*kapiert*) and 'comprehends' movement." [49] (An example of this would be in habitual actions.) [50]

"We are brought to the recognition," Merleau-Ponty continues, "of something between movement as a third person process and thought as a representation of movement — something which is an anticipation of, or arrival at, the objective and is ensured by the body itself as a motor power, a 'motor project' (*Bewegungsentwurf*), a 'motor intentionality' in the absence of which the order remains a dead letter" [51] (for example, the order to grasp).

There is this direct contact which somehow connects the normal body to the world (to use Merleau-Ponty's expressions, as "outline on the world," "potentiality of a certain world," "potentiality of certain regions of the world"); that is, there is this, "grasping of motor significances," this type of intuitive, nonformulated, immediate knowledge of the orientation and regulation of the attitudes and movements of the body that are directed toward one goal and one action in the surrounding world. This type of knowledge moves along quite smoothly and unconsciously in normal life, where everything happens so naturally and without complications. In certain illnesses, when it fails, it will be revealed better. The widely used example of cerebral lesions, such as the case of Schneider studied by Goldstein (and repeated by Merleau-Ponty), constitutes in sum an application of Bacon's method of variations. It is the failures of a function that best reveal existence, through the conspicuous disorders resulting from it, as the unintended noises reveal the presence of a hidden actor.

How do such patients behave? Without going into detail here (we will refer to the original experiences), the deficit never appears topographical and localized, but global and structural. It is not a movement or an elementary perception that is affected, but the whole of the subject's presence and behavior in his environment. According to Goldstein,[52] the reactions of a part of the body are always accompanied by modifications in the whole body and answers to the *significance* of the local excitation for the total organism. The sick person who cannot *show* an object in response to the command, substitutes by various means "the intention of showing, in so far as the situation gives a meaning to this intention of showing." [53] At the command to demonstrate or to grasp, the sick person "disposes himself in another fashion." [54] He operates through a detouring of the objective analysis. Spontaneous acts, when enclosed within a need (e.g., to scratch oneself if something itches), remain intact. With the sick person, on the contrary, it is different. At the command to scratch his leg, he cannot respond without a preparation that resolves the movement into a spatial problem of geometry; he locates in objective space the place of his hand and of his leg, as anatomical parts, and complicated calculations are needed for the simple goal of directing his finger in the direction of his leg.

In the man whom we call *normal,* such "reasoning" is immediate, implicit, lived, *included in the body itself.* The body manifests something of comprehension (in short, of the spirit) and of a type of knowledge, without having to pass through the express detour of intellectual knowledge and comprehension.

Thus one sees, in such sick persons, the attack on the *immediate intelligence of the body.* "It is the existential base of intelligence which is affected, much more than intelligence itself," writes Merleau-Ponty,[55] and he adds: "This type of life of significances which renders the concrete essence of the object immediately legible, i.e., this familiarity, is interrupted." The intentional arc "goes limp. . . . The world no longer has a physiognomy." [56]

Such observations conspicuously illustrate the pathology of dualism, this vice of abstract and objectifying thought, of the "intellectual," which the patients of Goldstein seem to put into practice: "the experience of the body is degraded into a representation of the body." Is it not, indeed, an abnormal and truly pathological attitude to consider "my body, which is my point of view on the world, as one of the objects of this world"? The normal and healthy comportment of the body, "which distort both physiological and psychological explications, is understood on the contrary in the perspective of being-in-the-world " (Merleau-Ponty).

Such is the conclusion, antidualist or monist (whichever term one prefers), that must be drawn from these analyses. " The union of the soul and the body," as Merleau-Ponty says, " is not sealed by an arbitrary decree from two external terms, the one object and the other subject. It is accomplished at each instant in the movement of existence."

III

It is remarkable that the discovery of the body-subject could come to us by such different roads as the difficult (nearly ineffable) thought of a Gabriel Marcel and the observations of Goldstein or Merleau-Ponty. However, although the ways are dissimilar, no one would judge them incompatible. However far we push the analysis of behavior, it will never lead us to the approaches of the immediacy of the I (that " I exist," before proving it, playing it, and knowing it). We will never obtain anything but an analogy of the subject in terms of the object.[57]

We would be wrong, it seems to me, to persist in this type of debarment regarding the objective analyses of the body-subject. In any case, however far we would progress in the other direction (that of a reflexive and regressive interior study such as Marcel's) toward the limits of a prereflexive immediacy, we would in no way pretend to touch upon the I itself. Indeed, to " touch upon it " would be to say that it would be object, not subject; this very pretension would be self-contradictory.[58]

The type of study devoted to the body such as we find in Marcel's thought has a completely relative immediacy. Such an interior approach, no matter how shorn of all objective mediacy it might be, is always guided by and filtered through a culture and a language. This is done negatively, in a sense, in saying what it could not be, in rejecting certain approaches, certain procedures, certain deceptive names. Thus considered, such a study could at best only indicate a road to us, invite us to utilize a certain access, or describe for us the preliminary conditions of an experience that remains beyond all undertaking, always keeping one step beyond our grasps. It involves a *perspective,* never a discovery of the subject, and even less an appropriation of the subject. It is a matter less of a success than of an always unfulfilled attempt, which leads the philosopher to the awareness that he will never be satisfied. This, however, is the sign that he is on the right path, and the contrary would be rather disquieting.

Now, what is the goal pursued by the analysis from an objective point of departure, such as that of Merleau-Ponty? The goal is nothing more or less than to procure for us (like the preceding, but beginning with different material and through different ways) a *perspective,* an *index* of the body-subject. The objective information that it enlists are so many clues leading to the thought that there is a corporeal I at the source of behavior, although this I does not show us its visage. It can hardly be suggested that such analyses " make present " the I; at most they show us the traces or the imprints of the body-subject, without ever making any pretense of grasping it. The presence of the body-subject is only implied in the very structure of the conducts that we observe.

As Gabriel Madinier has pointed out, the subject is never brought out except indirectly, through the intermediary of manifestations that point to it and that guide us toward it. " Everything is a sign in which man manifests his spirit without ever equalling the obscure inspiration which animates and orients it." [59] This remark is basic, and seems to me to be valuable for the undertakings of both Marcel and Merleau-Ponty. To be sure, neither the manner nor the spiritual convictions of these men come together. It is nonetheless remarkable to note an essential convergence in the intention and the result of their philosophic approaches. Despite an opposition of their departure points and a disparity of the materials utilized, the direction is the same: *to grasp the invisible presence of the subject behind the signs that manifest it bodily.* " It is in

reflecting on the signs produced," Madinier says, " that the subject proves itself and will attempt to know itself. . . . The
signs involved are not *substitutes* for a *reality* given outside of
them; they are *instruments* of an activity which cannot be
grasped except in thus exteriorizing them." [60]

Whether I proceed by an interior reflection or by an understanding of exterior messages (behavior), in any case the subject will never be anything for me but the ineffable, invisible,
inaccessible source. I cannot grasp it, but it grasps the world,
and it grasps itself as the already objectified subject. [61]

It will never do to treat the subject only as object. We should
be careful, in the course of the very process which opens the
body-object in order to arrive at the body-I, not to treat this
I in turn as a product of our regressive analysis. In fact, no
method, reflexive or structural, permits us to speak of subjective reality without denaturalizing it and pushing it into the
objectivication from which we intended to preserve it. The
meaning of the subject is *love*, and no dissertation could take
its place. Every hope to unveil the face of the I would be self-
contradictory; it would turn the I precisely into a face. Self-
understanding is always a mediate thing, which brings oneself
into proximity with the I without ever fitting onself to it. In
other words, the I is beyond that which we can say about it;
it radically escapes our speech about it. It is of another order,
and we will never be able to do anything but separate out
that which it is not (its substitutes and appearances). There
is no antinomy between the subjective approach and the
objective approach to the body-subject. But an intelligent inquiry will utilize one or the other, without permitting itself
to fall into the trap of either one: the one serves as an antidote
to the seductions of the other. To whomever would wallow in
a poetic and quasi-ineffable rumination of the I, it should be
recalled that he remains in the mediacy of the sign; to whomever would claim to reach the subject at the end of his be-
havior-dissecting scalpel, it should be recalled that he suggests
the subject to us only by allusion.

IV

The body-subject, then, is recognized by signs, but signs that are not deceptive. This is the end toward which the previously mentioned analyses should strive. My body is, in certain ways, moulded or " inhabited " by the soul; it is animated; it *is* soul (without giving to the word " soul " a technical meaning), rather than the soul having need of the body being *added*. Now, when I say that the body is expressive, and that it *expresses* me, I am saying nothing else.

Here we must indicate all the richness of the word " to express." First of all, there is the idea of extracting (the juice from the fruit), of showing on the outside that which is hidden, of rendering present that which is still absent, inaccessible, ungraspable (the subject, for example); finally, there is the idea of communicating a message to someone.

Expression begins at the initial pole of description in order to end at the terminal pole of work (*oeuvre*), in passing through the intermediate pole of the sign message.

At the initial pole, expression describes someone, not only his presence but also his nature, his character, all that he is, his genus, his race, his family, his shortcomings, his genius, his individuality, his personality. Expression is a flagrant offense, or to use another analogy, like the fingerprints left at the scene of a crime. The body then, and we will return to this, is the very organ of description: " the invisible man " does not express himself; he leaves no trace (neither scent nor silhouette). Thus expression is what *betrays* my presence and permits the diagnosis that identifies me.

At the intermediate pole, expression is also the message that I address to the world and through which I *describe myself* and *beckon*. I expressly and intentionally mark my presence, that I am there and who I am. Thus we move from description to sign: language, style, word, problems of communication, etc.

Finally, at the terminal pole expression fulfills and com-

pletes me. It was the effect; it is the cause. It goes out from
me, but through it I become, I transform myself. It empties
me, but I am brought forth from it. It changes me and will
in its turn be changed by the one whom it will have changed.
It is thus that we arrive at the idea of the work (oeuvre) as
the expression of a person, of an artist, of a creative genius; it
is a dialogue between the creation and its re-created creator.
The work, body of my body, expresses me as one extends,
completes, and perfects the physiognomy of someone. My
work is the extension of my fingerprints and of my handwrit-
ing characteristics, yet in the meanwhile it accomplishes a
therapeutic. This is why *expression* is at the two functional
poles of description and sign, of diagnosis and therapeutic; it
describes me and it creates me.

We will return to the bipolarity of expression (Part Two,
Chapter VIII). For the present I want only to recall that the
body marks the presence of a subject.

It is sufficient for me to observe a glance, the lines and the
mobility of a face, the allure of a gait, the agility, movement,
and form of the hands, to convince me of the spiritual nature
of the body.[62] A hand is a small intelligent animal, mischievous,
provided with a curious individuality. One can portray a hand
as one portrays a face. To a lesser degree, the bust and the
legs *express* intelligence, that is to say, an *intention;* all that is
needed is for them to begin a movement or to assume a certain attitude. There is an expression and a meaning in the
least movement, in the scarcely noticed gesture. There is meaning in the form, the configuration, and in the immobilities of
the body. Finally, there is meaning in the proportions and lines
of the body. The lines of the hand, the fingerprints, as well as
the physiognomy and appearances of the face, and handwrit-
ing, *express* a human being, a particular person. Not only do
these things help us identify him — they have first convinced
us that a human being is involved. A footprint on the sand or
a fingerprint on a piece of paper, an abandoned garment, a
glove, a shoe — in such things the body has left its imprint.

And it is not any imprint whatever; it is the imprint of the spirit, that is, it is an expression. Ordinarily one is aware only of elaborated expression, or expressions of a highly cultivated nature: drawings, writing, spontaneous or composed works. These are, undoubtedly, the most meaningful and the easiest to read due precisely to their differentiated characters. But my hand presents a portrait of me as a man that is just as striking as the fine lines of the hand that my hand draws on the piece of paper. A human hand directly expresses humanity, intelligence, spirit: it is corporeally intentional, the sign of the body-subject.

The body-soul dualism, and the idea which maintains that the body is an object animated by the soul capable of escaping from the body to live an independent life, seems to receive a semblance of proof from the spectacle of the *cadaver*.

The cadaver (and is it not the same for the unconscious man who in appearance cannot easily be distinguished from the cadaver? [63]) has lost something, the *expression* or the *presence*. His visage has become unexpressive, inert, *absent*. The cadaver is *posed* in a given position, from outside; the movements which it shows are only molded from outside, imitated: " One would *say* that he is seated, that he looks, that he points." But we know that he is a cadaver: indeed, the hand, the body, the visage itself (the most fragile of the body's regions, and, in that regard, the most susceptible of losing its expression) *remain imbued with the soul* in the cadaver itself. What I mean is that they conserve a line, a form, an attitude. And yet, it will be objected, the cadaver does not possess any of these things; it is inanimate. Does this not prove that this line, or form, or attitude have meaning only for us who give them an expression? What do the living visage and hand express by themselves if the visage and hand of the cadaver so easily give the illusion of an expression? Should we not bring in the image, at least approximate, of a soul superadded to the body, precisely in order to mark the difference between a cadaver and a living being?

Such considerations would prove, in my sense, at most the dualism of soul and cadaver. The cadaver retains the print and the expression of the genius that has marked it by its passage. But does not this show that such a dualism does not take account of the living body? The living body is different from the cadaver only through this intimate incorporation of the soul, of which the cadaver, somehow, has preserved a memory (in the immobile form and attitude of the hand, of the carriage of the head). If the hand of the cadaver still has a soul, it is because the soul is still there, in its form and attitude, which are the form and attitude of man's body.

To reject the dualist abstraction is not to affirm that the soul and the body are really one and the same thing (which would lead one to wonder why they are given two different names). But to conceive of them as distinct is not to conceive of them as separate. Antidualism discredits itself by wanting to prove too much. The body-soul duality does not exist in the healthy and living body; it *begins* in sickness as it intrudes brusquely on the spiritually defenseless being. This duality reaches its limit in death; it is vanquished by the resurrection which, precisely, is something completely different from the immortality of the soul; it is the resurrection of the body. Dualism is an error for the living body; it becomes a provisional verity for the cadaver. The equivocal nature of the word "body," which must be cleared up, comes from the fact that sometimes it designates the living body and sometimes the bodily appearance (a "chemical body," or "the body" spoken of at the funeral, i.e., the cadaver). In other words, it is life that negates dualism. Indeed, it is the characteristic of life to negate dualism, so that the very definition of life includes the indissoluble unity of body-soul or animated-body (which goes without saying). It is in this sense that resurrection is *life;* it overcomes dualism and reinstates together the soul-body, the animated-body.

When one ponders the mystery of man's origin in terms of *creation,* it seems that the creation of the soul and the creation of the body, although of different orders, belong to the same action of the Creator. The animation of the body comes not from an addition, but from a blossoming. The human body would not even be a body if it were not (animated with) a soul. It would be a framework, or a model, or whatever one likes, but it would not be a body. It is the soul that makes the body a body, that is, a form, an expression, an attitude, a movement as they are expressed in a man's visage or hand.

To say that a head or a hand are *expressive* is to acknowledge the soul or a subject in their mobility and dynamism; but it is equally to see them in their very *anatomy*. The anatomy of a body (of which the cadaver temporarily retains a memory) signifies the recovery or, in a sense, the transfiguration of a thing by a soul. This is true even to the point that my soul resides in my corporeality as well as in my personality and individuality, in the fibres and form of my corporeality as well as in its acts. My visage, my hands, my body, are of the visible, palpable, material soul, which is incarnate and present.

V

I have spoken of the cadaver, the petrification limit of the animated body, as the provisional requittal of dualism, but this requittal is already announced in the dissensions of the sick body. However, we have also seen that the flounderings of sickness make manifest the structural unity of the body (as matter-consciousness) *in the very degree to which this unity begins to break down.* The difficulty, then, is in showing both this unity and the beginning of its dissolution (in sickness in particular, and also in a more general fashion in the human condition, in which sickness figures as a sort of favored stigma). The ambiguity of sickness illustrates in halftones what we have said concerning the dead body.

In short, sickness furnishes evidence both of dualism and of monism. The flounderings give evidence of this unity through the beginnings of a rupture of the unity; and monism is brought to light through the nascent dualism.

How, then, can this unity-duality of the sick body be presented? It is *duality,* since it has served to show us the admirable unity of the healthy body; yet it is all the same *unity,* if it is true (as I pointed out in Chapter II) that sickness forms a type of "explanation" with life, that is to say, a global conduct that mobilizes and structurally reorganizes, down to the smallest cells, the entire body in a posture of defense and readaptation aiming at continuing life at any cost, but in a different manner.[64]

The relationship of the sick person to his sickness is ambiguous. It lends itself to a dualist perspective as well as to a monist perspective of the body.

As I said in Chapter I, the sick subject is at first sight someone for whom his own body becomes, to a certain degree, a *foreign body.* "He disposes of his body," writes Merleau-Ponty, "only as an amorphous mass." [65] But this foreign body sticks to him closer than Nessus' tunic. This is the paradox of the sick body, which is the very antithesis of the living body.

I never feel my body so much my own than when it makes me suffer. Would it do me harm if it were not me? As a related being, flesh of my flesh, it makes me suffer more than a stranger. But my sick body is infinitely close to me, yet contradictorily foreign. It is me — in a dualistic mode. It is mine, as one suffers an unavoidable traveling companion, chained together for life and death, and to whom one has taken a dislike. Sartre has written, in *No Exit,* "Hell is — other people." The sick body, in the same way, is precisely another, besieging me and clutching me in a deadly familiarity from which I am incapable of extricating myself.

Such, then, is the intimity-duality of the sick body. The debate concerning the violations of the person through therapeutic aggressions has previously given me the chance to pose in the following terms the ambiguity of dualism and of monism: "We must choose between a dualism which predicates an inviolable subject, no matter what alterations therapy or sickness inflict on the body; and a monism for which all intervention on a part of the body, however peripheral it might be, affects the soul and brings about a new psycho-organic structure, a new totality. This problem, which calls into question the scope of our therapeutics, is the same whether it involves psychosurgery or the amputation of a leg. In the same way, it should be understood that therapeutic aggression and the aggression of sickness are located on the same plane. For the dualist, I am distinct from what happens to me, be it physical or mental illness, medical or surgical treatment, operation on any organ or even on the brain itself.

" But the spiritualist, try as he may to believe in an inviolable soul capable of emerging intact at the end of long years of dementia, knows nevertheless that the person in his most personal freedom is not sheltered from a disintegration through illness. In reality, one cannot separate the subject who reacts to this mutilation, accepting it or rejecting it, from the part affected.

" To be sure, in law I can objectify the injury suffered; it remains peripheral. I am a citadel around which everything can change without myself changing. And my final attitude rests with me regarding the changes that happen to me, sickness, healing, psychoanalysis, etc. In reality, however, the separation is never so impervious that the center does not become more or less contaminated by the injury, no matter how peripheral it might be. Even the man who remains resolute after the amputation of his two hands knows that he has been reached and that his very manner of objectifying and dominating over the injury is colored by this injury. The separation is never quite complete. The meaning of an injury depends on me, but I am changed by it. My way of standing in opposition to it is, again, the injury itself. My manner of reacting against it comes through it. In other words, the mutilated being and the subject standing vis-à-vis it are distinct and nondistinct at one and the same time: dualism and monism form a true ensemble." [66]

Would I express myself otherwise today? Dualism seems to

me to be a permanent temptation and power, a promise and a menace. In any case, it seems to be a *right* that is inscribed in the very interior of a reality of *fact*, the body-soul or body-spirit structural unity (I will differentiate between soul and spirit in the next chapter; it is not important at this point). Similarly in the face of a dualism that splits the whole fabric of the body (as divorce breaks the unity of the couple that is one flesh), monism will appear, in turn, as a power, a promise, a permanent right of the person for the reconquest of the self.

VI

The ambiguity of the subject-object body bursts out in full in sickness. But sickness only activates and precipitates this ambiguity which belongs to our very humanity, to our human condition. There has been frequent emphasis of this strange paradox wherein my body, the closest to me of all the objects in the world, is at the same time the most opaque thing to me.[67] For my body-subject is an unknown. One knows it only by gaining a perspective on it, and by objectifying it. I do not make objective my endocrinal intimity. The realities that are most foreign to the subject are not the least known, quite the contrary. What is farther from me and more indifferent to my living body than mathematical reality, which I know clearly and distinctly? What is more intimate than my deep motives, which psychoanalysis brings into light and which thereby greatly surprise me, as if it were a matter involving an other, an unknown? The most mysterious for me is myself, more than any other being in the world. That which is too close blinds me, covers my eyes. I can see it only in putting it at a distance. And that which I can put at a distance from me, to detach from me and objectify, is that which I know best of my body, viz., my outside.

In reality, the ambiguity of my body is found once again in the double face that it offers to observation. One can never disconnect, with success, the internal from the external, and the external forms in unbroken continuity with the fabric of the universe. I grasp the universe, I am the universe through this umbilical cord, and the universe is in me through this same strange ambassador, my own body. My body is this bi-faced intermediary, this mediator; it is me and it is the universe; it is subject and it is object.

In order to make a start on the remaining part of my study, I will conclude these reflections on the "mixity" of the body-subject (and especially of the sick body) with two basic observations:

1. No matter how much of a stranger the body is felt to be by the subject (especially by the sick person), this body remains, whether we like it or not, the body-subject of a person assuming his life. I would have a difficult time rejecting my body, for it will be my witness. This is why I could say that the body is the revealer of our problems.

2. But I would add immediately that it is the revealer of our resources: if this witness will, in effect, be made anyway, with or without me, it behooves me that it be made with me, and for it to express the mark of my dignity and of my freedom.

It is the witness to my problems, of the manner in which I handle my problems, and of what they become through my attention. In fact, it is exactly the manner in which the sick person will assume his body and his life that will make this body either a *subject* or an *object*, pushing it in some way toward one pole or the other, toward a segregation of a dualist type or toward a postdualist recovery. Once more we slide from the level of the ascertainment to the level of the need.

One's body will therefore be what man's *choice* makes it (and we will see later on what this choice means): body-subject, if he is capable of taking it in charge; body-object, if he is incapable of it.

The body-object, then, appears as a residuum of a negative attitude, the result of a negative choice, of a resignation and (to use Marcel's term) of a repudiation. The *ethic* of sickness, as we will see, will have the task of overcoming this resignation.

The body-object signifies the objectified body, changed into an object, reduced to the objective state. And the objectivity of the body expresses, in sum, my refusal. It measures my refusal to assume and welcome my body, to allow myself to be penetrated by it, to be incorporated in it, to be incarnated in it, to recognize myself in it and to recognize it as being myself. The body-object expresses one particular attitude, among others, of man in regard to himself. I express myself here by antitheses, in order better to understand. The dualism which separates me from my body is not always a resignation. Consider Stoicism, for example. Dualism can represent a stage (the moment of the conflict) on the road that leads from asceticism to love, to reconciliation with the body and with the world. This is an evolution which is a revolution and a conversion, to be sure, but one also that forbids simplistic antinomies. What I mean is simply, to anticipate somewhat, that our body is, in the final analysis, what we make of it, that which we deserve. It expresses our problems and our resources: what I am and what I can be. It is the faithful image of my difficulties, of my shortcomings, of my secret conflicts; but it is also the portrait of my decisive choices and of the power of integration, assumption, and of witness of which I am capable.

CHAPTER IV

Psychosomatic Medicine and the Medicine
of the Person

I

THE STRUCTURAL UNITY WHICH WE HAVE JUST STUDIED UNDER
the name of the *body-subject* seems to me to contain the germ
of a principle that goes infinitely beyond the commonplace
interaction of the organic and psychic, such as a psychosomatic
medicine *stricto sensu* would understand it. In fact, this unity
constitutes (for those able to see it) the more profound and
more mysterious solidarity of the organico-psychic structure
itself with the *spirit* (in the nontemporal or transcendent
sense of the term).

This nuance (which is more than a nuance) will lead us into
considerations that are more properly speaking philosophical.
In these considerations we will come once again across the
classic distinction between soul and spirit, although we realize
that these terms are too variable and too disputed to lend
themselves to any settled definitions concerning their opposition. We therefore refuse to become involved in such a debate
and would avoid mentioning it were there not some basic consequences involved regarding our medical practice and the
anthropological presuppositions of our therapeutic itself.

I think that the major difference between the Medicine of
the Person and psychosomatic medicine resides in this shift-

ing of the focal point, which is no longer situated between the organic and the psychic, but between the organico-psychic and the spiritual.

Thus the Medicine of the Person will go farther than the elementary interdependence between the lesional and the psychological (whichever side one emphasizes), e.g., the role of cares, of shocks of infancy, the problems of life, depth psychology, etc. The Medicine of the Person directs its attention to the *unity of the psychosomatic and the spiritual;* and it is precisely this "compound" twice removed, or as it were, to the second power, this spirit-incarnate mixture, which constitutes the person.

II

But what part, one will ask, does the body play in the spirit? Indeed, we have seen the extreme difficulty of this inquiry in the exact area that it wishes to reach, for it would be absurd to contest the duality of the psychological and the spiritual (logical or transcendental, both of which designate the same reign).

It is universally accepted that judgment of *meaning* (logical or ethical), judgment of value, in short, judgment pure and simple,[68] belongs to the order of *right;* the psychological, on the contrary, is a *state of fact,* and no more.

From the time that one asks if a fact has, or does not have, meaning, one refers, like it or not, to an order completely different from that of the fact: the order of meanings or the order of truth. "The meaning of an activity," writes Ruyer, "does not lie in its literal unfolding. . . . A dualist conception of man is thus essential."[69] This is what he quite correctly calls the duality of the *spatial world* (the world of causes and effects connecting closer and closer) and the *transpatial world* (or intemporal) of meaning, which "flies over" the former, that is to say, which unifies the multiple, gathers together the end in the beginning.

Every man who pronounces a judgment (of meaning or of

truth) enters the world of signification — consciously or not, whether he is mistaken in the content of his judgment or not. This world of the mind orients not only meaningful human actions, but also the hidden finality that we lethargically decipher in the undertaking of life, of the embryo, of matter, of the electron, in short, of every individuality possessing a structure and a form. This undertaking maintains the stability and the individuality of this form throughout the changes of time.[70]

Every reality having a meaning, every judgment insofar as it puts forth a truth, implies a transcendent reality, an intemporal, nonpsychological, spiritual reality (an I, as opposed to the *me* that I actualize in the world).

We discover here so many manifestations of a particular activity that could be called *spiritual,* whose characteristic is the transformation of a brute fact into a significant fact. Another mark of this activity is the connecting of facts to other facts in a fabric, in a history having a meaning. The historical exists as such only by and for a transhistorical perspective, that is, a witnessing to the spirit. " There would be no history for a purely historical being," writes Jean Lacroix.[71] History is a history only by the spirit that dominates over it and makes of it precisely a history. Gabriel Madinier writes, " In order for consciousness, which is temporality, to understand itself as temporal, it is quite necessary for it to escape temporality through some point of itself." [72] Consciousness, in reality, is outside of time by the very act of comprehending time as time.

The fact as fact, the world as such, the me as me, the subject as subject, are comprehended by a subject who, in doing so, is marked out as an extramundane subject, *I*. It is necessary *not* to be what one is in order to be able to say what one is; one must escape what one is, mortal, fallible, etc., in order to recognize oneself as mortal, fallible, etc. In short, dualism is contained in the act that expresses it, either to deny it or to affirm it; it is contained in what affirms it and in what denies it.

Phenomenological analyses such as that of Husserl have, in their turn, reminded us with new force and rigor of the duality of fact and meaning, of the psychological and the spiritual. "The primary end of logical research," writes Gaston Berger, "is to make a radical distinction between logic and psychology, . . . between the anthropologically subjective unity of knowledge and the ideally objective unity of knowledge, . . . between the psychological act through which laws are laid down and their ideal essence towards which the concrete thoughts of individuals strain (intentionality)." [73]

Let us conclude in these terms: it is a *fact* that, for man, the *fact* does not suffice. It requires its very precise justification, namely, *the right of being*, i.e., a meaning, a value, a truth. Now, to require justification or the reason for a fact is to judge, to lay down a truth or a value. It is to refer to an order found "outside" of the fact itself, the order of the valid and the invalid, of right and wrong, in short, to the order of another part that is accessible to every human being, spiritualist or materialist. It is to unveil, at last, the absolute of the spirit as the point of *reference*, without which there is neither right nor wrong, valid nor invalid, but only brute facts.

III

I have simply wanted to recall this *radical* duality of fact and meaning, of the temporal me and the spiritual subject "I" which situates it. This duality, regarding all philosophical or nonphilosophical reflections, best describes our situation. We are body and outside of the body; we are in time and outside of time. We are eternal and temporal. We are the site of a *transcendence*, whether we like it or not, whether we are conscious of it or not, whether we affirm it or deny it. It is in this sense that we understand the *liberty* and the *spirit* through which we go beyond the gravitational pull of determinism and the literal unfolding of cause and effect — in order to judge them.

However, it should be emphasized that to be the seat of transcendence, and inhabited by it, by no means leads us to recognize transcendence as such. Between these two experiences there is an abyss that is impossible to cross except by a radical leap, a sudden self-awareness, a conversion of one's perspective, indeed, almost a religious conversion.

In what consist the relationships between *the fact of going beyond the fact* (which we have called the fact of the transcendence of man) and *the meaning or the discovery of transcendence?*

They are narrow, yet blind relations. Throughout his entire life, *man can be ignorant of the god that dwells in him.* The understanding (in the primary sense), which is exercised in the least value judgment, has not turned its attention on this transcendence. Yet man is able, in various ways, to discover the god dwelling in him. He is able, through a rational approach, to know the transcendence that is in him, without thereby perceiving the transcendence that is the source of his own. In order to move from the first approach to the second, it would be necessary:

1. either to elaborate no less than a metaphysic of the Cartesian type, for example, which would lead from the idea of the infinite to the idea of the only possible source of this idea;

2. or, more simply and more profoundly than any metaphysic, to discover that which is a great deal more than the obviousness of an intellectual interdependence, i.e., to discover the existential meaning of God, to perceive and recognize God. Such an encounter can, in its turn, be as obscure, malformed, undeveloped as a dazzling birth; or it can break through in the framework of a religious tradition and a language. The first type would be exemplified by religious feeling or a Jungian feeling of the "numinous." Such are the experiences that our colleague Prof. Graf von Dürckheim seeks to call forth in the patients who consult him. The second type would be exemplified by the encounter of the risen Christ, the incarnate Word. Let us explain this in more detail.

The encounter of the living God is an autonomous, direct, decisive experience, like that of Moses on Sinai, that of Paul

on the road to Damascus. This encounter, of course, comes
about neither by becoming aware of the transcendence that
dwells in me, nor by an approach of the Cartesian type. It is
direct contact, either (within the Christian faith) with the God
of Jesus Christ, the life of the Holy Spirit and of the Sacraments
in us, or (outside of all religion or within a religion) directly
with the Creator of all things, the source of all creatures, the
" englobing." Truly, it always involves a sense of the sacred. It
always involves a religious experience, even outside of all differentiated religion.[74]

I am spirit, I am source. However, my source is in the Spirit.
The experience of God, the sense of the transcendent in general, is the feeling of my entire dependence on and belonging to
the absolute source of life, to Someone who is All and who is
Personal. This feeling begins a movement that is the putting of
my very destiny and freedom in his hands, the returning of my
will to the hands of God. The meaning of my life belongs to
him. This involves not only a knowledge but an entire attitude,
a kneeling, and an adoration. Moreover, this attitude is nothing
other than the attitude of poverty, the opposite of sufficiency.
Not to listen to oneself, but to hear and welcome another
word, to permit oneself to be taught, to give up trying to be
clever and to make oneself the measure of all things. Such an
approach, the existential humility of the poor (of the *anavim*),
offers us the equivalent of a metaphysic and even more. It
leads directly to the Spirit without the detour of reasoning, in
life itself.

The problem, for me, consists, however, of pointing to the
junction of the two transcendences which, according to customary terminology, bear the names " ascending transcendence " and " descending transcendence." The first designates
precisely the consciousness of the god that dwells in me, that
is to say, the consciousness of my dualizing power that allows
me to go beyond temporality and the brute fact, through the
approach of truth, value, and meaning.[75] The second designates the perception of the dependence of my independence,

my belonging to a source of transcendence, who is God.

The two transcendences can preclude each other. The atheistic approach, in particular, acknowledges, invokes, and magnifies the first against the second, which is considered as the projection and the rival of the first. My transcendence superhumanizes me, and its constant temptation is to project itself into a divinity in its own image, to alienate itself in this projection.

In this impasse, the becoming aware of my human transcendence, which is a magnificent discovery, erects the obstacle barring the way to the *meaning* of transcendence, which could have been more readily perceived without this awareness. The autopositioning is shortcircuited on itself and becomes opposition. The opposition is always contained within the autopositioning. It is not a question of avoiding the moment of opposition, which is a necessary moment. It is, however, necessary to guard against the immobilization and installation of this moment. That is, this moment must not become hardened into a dualism as we have previously explained. The danger is that it will become hardened in an atheism or rather in an absurd self-sufficiency of man.

In reality, this barrier is only inconsequential. Descartes understood this quite well in his approach, which illustrates perfectly the passage from the becoming aware of the transcendent or the spiritual *in man* to the becoming aware of transcendence that is the infinite source of it. I am finite and imperfect, and yet I move beyond this imperfection and finitude through my power of locating them and of knowing them as such. But how can I know them as such without referring to the infinite and the perfect? Whence come these references (the infinite, the perfect) if the imperfect and the finite do not provide the source of them? Does the finite contain the infinite? Only the infinite can give me the idea of the infinite. My source comes from outside. The divine transcendence is the source of my transcendence; the Spirit is the source of my spirit (which, Descartes adds, is absolutely other than my body, is *doubled* with my body). Descartes went to the extreme, from a discovery of the absolute originality of the spiritual to a mechanistic dualism regulating the body on the level of a machine. The step was a logical one, even for someone who had studied anatomy (of the cadaver, it is true). It is equally true that Descartes, in his turn, has belied the commentators who would enclose him in a mechanistic dualism.

More simply, and without going through metaphysical subtleties, when I have become aware of my own transcendence through the duality of fact and of meaning (in other words, of the presence of the spiritual, which cannot be confused with the psychological), I realize that I cannot encounter *my own transcendence* without wondering about the foreignness of that which I have discovered. To be sure, one can quite well stop there, absurdly placing this infinity in my finitude. This is the irrationalism of an obstinate rationalism that blocks its own passage, that fixes itself in the absurdity of an ascertainment that is anything but rational! What must be attempted is a movement from the consciousness of a transcendence in me to the meaning of the transcendence which is the source of it, to which it refers intellectually (Descartes, for example) and existentially (conversion of faith).

The direct experience of transcendence (let us say religious in the broad sense) bursts forth in certain limiting circumstances (deportations, the major trials of life) through a limiting attitude which itself, in the total deprivation of *nothing*, discovers suddenly the overabundant fullness of *all*. Such an experience is not at all rare, and its existential paradox has been remarkably underlined by Kierkegaard.[76] These situations of rupture throw us literally off our hinges; we become abruptly vulnerable, open, our defenses down. Life, all of a sudden, forces us to unburden ourself of ourself, to die to ourself. Like a fruit that falls from the tree to the ground and opens at the shock, we become open to transcendence. We perceive a certain presence and a certain contact that our habits and our life situation normally make us pass by indifferent, blind, and deaf. The limiting trials render us poor, and the poverty is welcome. Then we listen ("Hear, O Israel"), we pay attention, we perceive. Transcendence overtakes us, or as Péguy said, "soaks" us. Indeed, joy surges from the very depths of distress, cutting through suffering, completely separate from suffering, bringing it an unexpected and mysterious refutation: "I am free, Brand, I am free," writes Ibsen's Agnes. The presence of God is the very same.

Many names are possible for this presence; and innumerable techniques are used to facilitate the eruption of this contact, through the word, through the experience of certain elementary exercises that bring us to discover the duration, the existence, the "being-there" (e.g., contemplation, prayer, even breathing alone, the elementary act of looking, of listening, of eating, of sitting, of waiting in silence, or relaxing, of detaching oneself from the self, of contemplating an object or a landscape. There is a postural, respiratory, and muscular experience of transcendence, which struggles to make it tasted and *touched*, as one struggles to make the word perceived by a deaf-mute through the movement of the lips.

IV

But the barrier of reasonings and quibbles hinders one from understanding that transcendence is in us, that it touches us, that the spirit dwells in us and lifts us out of the self. This barrier hinders us from realizing the mystery of this experience. This mystery is that we are temporal and nontemporal, *of this world here below and not of this world.* And this mystery is found in the least of our judgments, in the least of our affirmations and negations concerning the truth or meaning of this or that.

It would be necessary, preliminarily, to tear down this barrier. And the first thing that should be dispensed with is the purely academic idea that all the experiences to which I allude can be reduced to behavior patterns, or ideologies, or

ideological " superstructures," which are in turn the pure prod-
ucts of social and biological substructures. Our convictions
(and why not those of he who opposes us?) would then be
conditioned reflexes infinitely more complex than those of
Pavlov, but of the same order.[77] In this respect it would be useful to recall, as Ruyer does in his book on Neo-Finalism, that
" to affirm that every act is a pure effect of causes . . . is to offer
an absurdity parallel to that of the insane person who says: ' I
am dead,' or ' I do not exist.' For whoever affirms something,
affirms it as true, and acknowledges that he has sought the
truth, which is fundamentally inconsistent with the fact of having been actuated by pure causes. . . . Take, for example, a
behaviorist who would affirm that the behavior of human beings, himself included, is always capable of being described in
terms of stimulus-response; furthermore, this stimulus-response
tie, which is so complicated that it can exist through intermediary mechanisms, always has the nature of a causal chain
and is realized by degrees. Now, then, if the words or writings
of this behaviorist are simple responses to stimuli (Pavlovian,
or superstructures), how and by what right does he feel he is
right over against his adversaries? His responses, like the
reddening of the sunflower, are real facts. But *fact* is not
synonymous with *true* (or false) *proposition,* and the responses
of his adversaries are just as much facts as his own." [78] This
is true in such a way that if I say to the person who denies
transcendence, " You are right; it is as you have stated," then
the approbation which I give to him is a refutation of that
which he has stated! *A pure effect can be neither right nor
wrong.* It is inherent in causalist doctrines to be refuted by
approbation as well as by criticism (Ruyer, *op. cit.*).

I feel that it would be useful, by a dialogue of this type, to
bring the materialist patiently to sense, one day or another, the
transcendence that dwells in him. Through this he will become
opened to another world where he is at home. And then he will
learn that it does not come from him. Two stages are involved.
In the first, it must be shown that each of us, through the least

of our judgments of meaning, truth, or value, is of this world and of an "other"; we must be brought to feel this "other" world of which we are (this other world that is not "elsewhere," in a "beyond," but right here, in ourselves). In the second stage, the wonderment in the face of this duality that dwells in us must open us to the mysterious source of this duality. This approach will bring us from the intimate feeling of our transcendence to the feeling of the transcendence in which our own participates and from which it *receives* the spirit.

It is quite true that demonstration and argumentation are useless here. We must be shown, made to see, put into a condition in which we can realize for ourselves that which no one else can realize in our place. There is a step that no person can make for us in our place. "Debate, discussion, arguments, contradictions, adversaries," are so many words or attitudes that risk falsifying the dialogue, of putting it on a terrain that betrays the very object that it involves and the very spirit in which one must contemplate it. The aid of sympathy and confidence between interlocutors is absolutely indispensable, as is the sympathetic approach that disposes one to listen to the other as a friend (a friend who in no wise means to force an adversary into a corner, but who leaves the other to challenge and teach himself). This is not at all an easy thing to do and can always be misunderstood. It is necessary to realize this and to wait until the right time.

V

It is necessary to understand transcendence, to gain a feeling and a tact for the spirit in us and for the Spirit from which our spirit receives all that it is. "But," one will ask, "how does this concern a study dealing with the body; what does it have to do with physicians?" I would point out that a little bit of philosophy drives one away from practice; a little more brings one back again. Thus with the preceding considerations: they are basic in an anti-, or better, *postdualist* study on the body precisely to the extent that allowance is made for a dualism (which some would prefer to call a " trialism " of the body, soul, and spirit). The importance of this dualism could not be slighted without devaluating considerably the very unity of our corporeality.

Let us say immediately that the primary utility of a discovery of the spirit concerns both physicians and patients.

1. The physician must realize that the patient in front of him cannot be reduced to a chain of conditionings, that he is spirit and person. The physician must also realize that the patient, in turn, regards him and can reduce him also to the state of an object or an instrument. The operation of objectification or of " instrumentization " is not a one-way street. It is important to guard against its being produced in either way. Psychoanalysis, which puts the accent on the phenomena of transfer and countertransfer, is in less danger than other medical approaches of forgetting the essence of the interpersonal *relationship*, since psychoanalysis makes this relationship the essence of the therapeutic itself. But there is a danger of objectifying this relationship under the form of a technique (that is, just one more technique). The patient then becomes the object of application of this technique, just as the physician can become for his part. To discover the spirit is to discover the person whom one has before him in the person of the patient. This is, I would say, to discover the form of Christ in one's neighbor, whoever he might be.[79] And when one has recognized the Spirit in this spirit, when one has recognized Christ in his patient because one has located his patient in Christ, then the physician will regard the patient in a different perspective, with a different hand and with a different therapeutic quality.

2. An equally remarkable utility is that the patient learns to receive the Spirit. This reception of the Spirit comes not only in his physician (the reciprocal approach of the preceding), but in himself. Another quality of reaction will be born of the recognition. There will be another quality in the rela-

tionship of trust with the man who treats him. There will also be a difference in his way of understanding, of accepting and battling in one and the same effort. His resources will be different, his style of healing, his way of dying or of facing the deteriorations of chronicity. There will be another quality of life in the event of this trial which we call illness. The complaining attitude of being poorly used gives way to joyous and confident combat.

When the patient adopts the attitude " which is correct" (von Dürckheim), when he is able to find the " correct" attitude of the body (which is the attitude of the soul), the true way of " holding himself " (physically and psychically), he is put into a better healing position. He is no longer the same, because he will have realized, by and through his illness and with the aid of the physician, the strengths of the Spirit, the intervention and the participation of the source of all our strength. The fish that sickness has thrown out of its natural habitat finds itself borne and sustained anew by its element, the universal dynamism, in Christ.

VI

For certain reasons we have felt it indispensable to recall with some insistence the radical duality of fact and meaning, of the temporal and the spiritual subject which transcends it, of the psychological and the logical (that is, the nontemporal, or spiritual). Now, indeed, we come to the heart of the difficulty, the mystery of our body, of our personal unity, of our corporeality, of our incarnation, *despite or, rather, in this very duality.*

For the philosopher it would undoubtedly be necessary to locate oneself, as I have attempted elsewhere,[80] in a perspective analogous to that of Piaget when he studied " the psychology of intelligence." It seems contradictory to envisage the development in individual and collective history, and the genesis in time, of laws of the spirit, which is outside of time. The axiomatic, the laws of the intelligence, are outside of time, outside of the body, outside of psychology. Nevertheless, a psychology of the intelligence is possible, that is, a *genetic* of the *axiomatic* which illuminates the concrete and biopsychological attachments of the spirit.

The duality of the psychological and the spiritual is fulfilled in their vital unity. "It is not a question of two regions of the individual, but of two perspectives on the individual. . . . It is necessary to affirm the unity, continuity, and convertibility between judgment (the moral or spiritual exigence), on the one hand, and the psychological feeling, on the other hand. The one becomes the other and declines only in the other. The same material supplies the psychological and the spiritual. Or rather, the psychological and the spiritual are two ways of taking account of one and the same human reality. According to one's perspective, this reality becomes objectified and psychological *fact*, a pure established fact, a 'conduct,' or, on the contrary, the testimony to meaning or to truth, which is no longer in the domain of facts but of right. In man, value clothes the species of illness, and the eternal is the temporal there." [81]

I would express myself no differently now in saying that, in man, *the spirit clothes the species of the body, and that this is what we call a person.*

The second part of this study will attempt to make understood and to sense (and not to demonstrate, for we are now beyond the range of explication) the mystery of our corporeality and of our incarnation (the two are not necessarily the same thing). This mystery makes us, as individuals, one single man of spirit and body, although the spirit and the body do not cease to belong to two orders that are radically distinct and without common extent.

PART TWO

THE BODY, SIGN OR SACRAMENT OF THE SPIRIT

IT HAS BEEN NECESSARY TO GO THROUGH THE FOLLOWING TWO perspectives precisely in order to go beyond them.

1. The obvious role played by our body in our lives and in our thoughts; our mood through our "humors" ("One has the character and opinions of the glands and the stomach," and vice versa).[82]

2. The body is not an instrument, but "instrumentist" (Gabriel Marcel); it is not object, but subject. To be sure, it forms a structural unity. However, this is not only psycho-organic (or vice versa), but also psychospiritual.

Thus we come to this last stage, which is difficult but essential in a study concerning the body.

As we have pointed out, the I is, unquestionably, "nonobjectivable." It is beyond space and time. It is eternal. It remains when the self flows out and is metamorphosed. It represents my permanence and my identity in the very course of my mutation.[83] *The I is outside of my body.* How, then, do we understand that it is body, and that the body is subject? We understand its corporeality precisely by emphasizing the transcendence of the I, of the spirit in relation to the body. To say that it is a matter of an immersion or of a descent into the body is to slip once again into the fatal terminology of dualism. The incarnation of the body is the spirit become body, embodied, actualized, living.

This is, of course, different from psychosomatic medicine; yet it is nonetheless a part of the most incontestable domain of medicine, as will be evident throughout our discussion.

I must consider my body not only as *condition* but also as *component,* beyond psychic facts and beyond the logical category itself.[84] My body is a constituent of the transcendence of thinking thought. It gives a temporality to the eternity of this thought. The genius of Péguy brings us invaluable aid with his language, in order to try to clarify and express that which transcends intellectually classified concepts. This temporal-eternal body-thought escapes explicative categories (which are dependent precisely on the order of the object). Yet, nevertheless, our language is that of the object. All that we can do is unveil, clarify, make understood, and ourselves understand our own enigma, which is that of being a body-subject.

It should be pointed out that the plan followed in the first part of this book will not be followed continuously in the second part. Some aspects will undoubtedly be covered again, from a different perspective. In the first part I analyzed the relationships (the distinctions and the connections) between the body and the person, through an emphasis on the spirit, the intelligence of the body, the spiritual virtues of the body.

In the second part, I will deal with the corporeal virtues of the spirit and with what is more properly called the incarnation, in short, with the "*materialism*" of the spirit. The psychological description will be taken up again, but as the sign and description of a spiritual reality (we will have to recall this in the course of our discussion).

Although some chapters will remain theoretically oriented, the accent will be put above all on the practical and poetic affirmation and on the moral and spiritual exigencies.

In this second part I will try to examine more thoroughly our corporeality. This will be done in two stages:

1. I will show that the body is cogenitor of thought (which

is, in reality, a thought-language, a gesture-thought). Above all, I will show that my body is, at one and the same time, the locus of my individuation and its surpassing (the body being the very thing which permits me to surpass it). I will call this first stage a *description* of corporeality.

2. In the second stage (which could more properly be called an *ethic,* for it will formulate a demand and an exhortation), I will state that my body constitutes the locus of my basic choice (the sign of the role I play in the world). My attitude regarding my body will be my attitude regarding the world; what diverts me from one will divert me from the other; what leads me toward one will lead me toward the other, so as to take on both with the same *élan,* with the same effort, the same hope.

In short, the body is not a *region* of the person; it is the very "face" of the person, where one can read the wishes of the person. The body is not simply that through which the spirit becomes a singular person; rather, it is through the body that the person witnesses to its spirit, to the spirit.

It is through my body that I accept or refuse this witness of the spirit; from this refusal results the body-object, the body-residue, the nonassumed body. The body is the interpreter, the translator, the revealer, the catalyzer, the spokesman, the herald who proclaims — in short, the body is the symbol of my *choice.* It is the mediator of the spirit.

Let us point out now that choice, attitude, and refusal are not necessarily located on the level of the deliberative consciousness. They concern more the deep levels of our spiritual life, that is, of the life of the spirit in us. These are levels which are both invisible and visible, both to our view and to that of others. This is no longer the psychological level, but the spiritual. It is the level of our verity, which does not always correspond to our psychological appearance (far from it).

There are, then, two parts: the one is descriptive and the other is ethical; the one develops the *fact* of our incarnation (which I would rather call our *corporeality*), and the other develops our *choice of incarnation,* that is, our corporeality rendered conscious, taken up again, confirmed, willed, espoused, assumed, consecrated (after the example of the incarnation of the Word, which somehow descends to meet our ascent toward him, and with whom we must attempt to examine relationships). But the separating of these two artificially successive parts would be fatal. It would betray the object of our discussion (the body-subject) if we were not to show at each step the joint uniting them, uniting the *fact* to the *choice,* the *choice* to the *fact.*

For instance, what does the body of the sick infant mean to him? What does the body of the very old person (in his second childhood, as we say) mean to him? Can one still speak of a choice or of a refusal of their corporeality? In such limited examples and limited consciousnesses, what qualifications will be discerned between the *fact-corporeality* and its assumed or, on the contrary, endured meaning (the choice of incarnation)?

There is a human region within which the fact and the choice are obscurely mixed, and I will try to identify it. This region is precisely the one that concerns us together, as physicians and patients. It is not something that we discourse on in sermons about perfect health. Nor will we ask the patient, at grips with his pain and anguish, whether he endures or whether he assumes his incarnation and understands it. The body speaks a direct language that knows neither words nor distinctions of " body-object " and " body-subject." The choice manifests itself — to the profundities of old age and to the luminous shadows of infancy, to the frontiers of the unconscious and of death. The choice decodes itself, with difficulty yet with completeness, in the forms, the attitudes, and the characteristics of the body, the face, the hands, the way of turning one's head, of sitting down or of eating, of smiling, of sleeping.

CHAPTER V

Thought *Is* Language, Spirit *Is* Body

THE POINT INDICATED IN THE CHAPTER HEADING IS AN ESSENTIAL
one. It is not of direct concern to our project of an anthropological study directed to physicians, to the potentially ill public, and to the potentially healed patients. Consequently, this
point of anthropological language will occupy me only briefly.

The body is indeed the *sine qua non* condition of all human
thought, insofar as it is human and insofar as it is thought.
One does not think without the body, because one does not
think without *language*. Carrying on a philosophic tradition
that ties thought to movement (i.e., to the body), the works of
my teacher, Gabriel Madinier, have attempted to elaborate a
motor theory of consciousness, in responding to this question:
" What is the role of movement (muscular) in thought, in the
act of becoming aware, in the formation of an interiority? " [85]

At first sight, a gestural theory of thought (by means of language) would seem to leave aside all forms of languageless
communication, giving prominence to the discursive to the
detriment of the intuitive. But what is true of spoken language
is also true of this language that goes beyond words and
phrases, that expresses the inexpressible and the ineffable, this
mute language of one's presence, of one's look, of that I-don't-
know-what that is the special warmth of a presence, even when

I do not see it. Someone stands behind me. I sense him, I feel
by a diffuse intuition his menace, his anger, his affection, his
tender feelings toward me. There are " presentiments " in present space, just as there are premonitions in time. There is a
" beyond " of language, but this beyond is, in turn, a language.
Even more than is true of spoken words, this other language
radiates directly from our body, without the intermediary of
the conventional signs that we call words.

Words are the bodies of our body, and implicit language dis-
penses with them, moving immediately through warmth, sympathy, even telepathy. The spirit expresses itself, then, without socialized intermediaries; but it would not express itself
and would not exist without the body.

I do not want to raise the question of telepathic or long-
distance communication. We understand very imperfectly the
nature of such communication, and can say nothing of either
its validity or invalidity concerning its corporeality or its visible or invisible materiality; however, is not wireless telegraphy
an " immaterial " material transmission? Yet, in any event, the
body is the direct (through the languageless language) or in-
direct (through words) mediator (not the instrument or organ) of communication, and even more so, of thought, reflection, of becoming aware, of the " formation of interiority "
(Madinier), which are also aspects of an inter- or intra-personal
communication. In short, consciousness is *gestural.*[86]

The unformulated, formless, and quasi-nonexistent (in proportion as a language, differentiated or not, does not cause it
to be in a body) is revealed to itself as *potential or nascent
movement.* For example, we talk about having something " in
the fingers " or " on the tongue." The study of memory disturbances, which are in reality difficulties of mnemic *recalling,*
confirm this basic principle.[87]

The pan-memory which, in each of us, accumulates all our
past, is actualized by means of the brain, which Bergson com-
pares to a filter through which we call to mind a given item.
If it were not for this vigilant guard, we would be submerged

by our past; and the brain, as Bergson paradoxically puts it, would serve to forget rather than to recall.

Our memory is an organ of selecting of motor and corporeal nature: by limiting the spirit, which brims over (if we can speak thusly of a reality of a different order), the body actualizes it. Is it not reasonable to conclude that the spirit-subject is independent of the body-instrument? There is no doubt an independence, and Bergsonian analysis brings to the matter a confirmation of the radical duality of the transcendent in relation to the psycho-organic, of which we have spoken in Chapter IV. However, this independence of *meaning,* or logical independence, does not imply an existential independence (with the corollary of *a survival of the disincarnated soul,* to which Bergson alludes [88]). The independence is in the meaning. By that I mean that these aspects of man belong to radically different orders, but they cannot conceivably be separated by any metaphysical process of disincarnation. In any event, the " immortality of the soul " remains a metaphysical theory, and nothing in experience authorizes one to profess it. We will see later that care should be taken not to confuse the Christian resurrection of the body-subject with the Orphic and Platonic theory of the immortality of the soul.

Consider our sensations: the most elementary sensation is in no wise passive. It is a movement that proceeds through the object through motions at least imperceptible to the eye, the muscles, the sense of touch, etc. The most silent of interior languages requires, for its part, the mobilization of phonatory organs. It is perception especially that has given rise to studies showing that the act that one assumes to be receptive is principally transmissive. To perceive is to cut up the object into pieces and minutely examine it; it is to master the object like a victim, to encroach upon it, to be thrown forward. Consciousness is always *ex*-istence; it is " intentional," breaking out toward the world. This intentionality, which is the attribute of logical processes, does not exist without the gesturality of a perception, of a recalling to mind, of a formulation, which be-

long to the psychological order. The "constituting spiritual
activity" of Lachieze-Rey, for example, "can be realized only
through a motory collaboration." [89]

It is not a question, for us, of *reducing* thought to movement
(Chapter IV protects us from this error). On the other hand,
this gestural "collaboration" must not be understood on the
kinetic or athletic level. "It is the motory intention more than
its externally observable realization that is of interest to us." [90]
The Bergsonian "motor schema" is not an observable fact. It
is not a thing, but an *act;* and it is always a characteristic of
an act to present the two sides of a spirit-matter Janus, to
present a spiritual aspect and a material aspect, in short, to be
body.

Madinier insists that it is not a question of reducing the act
of understanding to a movement, but of showing that the act
of understanding is not actualized, *does not exist,* without
movement. "What we are interested in is finding out why intelligence is actualized only under the species of movement,
why thought must be acted in order to be thought, and what
consequences result from this regarding its exercise." [91] This
movement is essential for the formation of thought, whether
the movement be peripheral and capable of being recorded, or
purely "central" (Dr. Mourgue), or "postural" (the motory
attitudes of accommodation or of preadaptation) and related,
in varying degrees, to the general tonicity of the body. The
motory or postural schema is, itself, neither perceived nor rep-
resentable: it is that through which, and with the aid of
which, I perceive or represent everything. It is the *condition*
of appearance of the object as object and is discerned only *in*
the object. It is implied in this constituting of the object, as
mediator between the object and the subject. Obviously it is
necessary to guard against a physiopsychological empiricism
and of making thought somehow descend into the body as into
a recipient. Incarnation (in the nonreligious sense) is not an
immersion in a body. It is incarnation, that is, that to compare
it or to assimilate it to something else is to betray it. The body,

as act, is not a thing, but "precisely the moment where form actualizes matter, where intelligence organizes the sensible world." [92]

For Pradines, "thought itself has a motory base." [93] The discerning of simultaneous data "consists of a mental and, at least imaginatively, motor oscillation."

Merleau-Ponty (cf. Chapter III) shows how my body is inserted in the world, how it mediates my being to the world. Biran's type of experiments, on their side, through the interplay of rest and effort, of resistance and movement, reveal the body as the locus of my opposition to the world, of the distinction between subject and object. In sum, *I am in the world* and *I am distinct from the world*, both at the same time, through my mediator-body.

This differentiation of the ego has been studied in the infant; the infant learns that he is *I* through movement. It could then be wondered what consciousness of the body could be gained by the infant confined to his bed and hindered by illness. The immobilized body is a poor conductor, or poor mediator. The infant knows himself by setting himself over against himself, and he does this by shifting his position and in the very resistance of the exterior world to his movement: a complete immobility, or one reduced to a few impotent resistances, would end only in an imperfect self-consciousness. Immobility is dissolvent; it dissolves me in the cosmos, and suffering itself is no longer perceived, distinguished, localized, or circumscribed as such or as mine. At the limit, *there is* diffuse and cosmic suffering. I am entirely suffering and disappear in an anonymous world of suffering. In brief, the becoming aware of the self by the sick infant depends on the duration and the nature of the illness: short, localized, nonimmobilizing, it is the mediator of consciousness and of human maturation; long and encroaching, it operates in the contrary direction and hinders this maturation. Consciousness is born of the difference. The body is the organ of the difference (cf. the following chapter); the sickness can by turns stimulate or block the mediator-catalyzer body. We have said that sickness activates or reactivates the dualist moment. Now we see that it can extinguish or stifle it as well.

There is consciousness only through action; there is action only through the body. This aphorism is verified even in the domain of the most abstractly intellectual thought. Such thought could not come into existence without taking on (a) body, without being made concrete, fixed, called into a body. *Signs are bodies of our body,* and a study of the relationships of language and thought does not fail to confirm the experience of the mediator-body.

Man dominates his action and the world not so much because he knows how to suspend action and gain perspective, but because he knows how to act in suspension or parenthetically, thanks to the subtle movement of language. "The sign is a movement," Madinier says, "a sublimated and sharpened movement." "Words are microscopic and infinitely supple motions." They originate as movements, through opposition and separation; they run through the object and occupy it as an army occupies the conquered battlefield. The opposition through the sign constitutes me as a subject. The sign is our best tool for analysis and synthesis: it constructs the object, space, and time; it makes distinctions and it unifies; it objectifies and it moves beyond objectification. It has been stated that difficulties with language coincide with an inability to manipulate space and to orient oneself in it. "Language difficulties lie in a more profound difficulty with the sense of space (i.e., at the depth of the *symbolic function*). Symbolic consciousness would be a gestural consciousness, a manipulation of time and space." [94] "It is because the sign is a movement that we must understand it not as a substitute for a ready-made and pre-existent thought, but as an instrument for a thought that is created; because it is an act, all thought is symbolic." [95]

The body is thus constitutive of the person even in his most thinking activity, because it gives thought an existence and

(a) body, and because no thought exists (at least in the human sense) without signs, without language, without body.

More than a type of photographic revealer of the spirit, the body constitutes the very existence of the spirit. *It causes spirit to be*, to the degree that, to our eyes, a nonincarnated thought is absolutely unthinkable,[96] a limiting idea as abstract as the idea of nothingness, for example (which, as Bergson has pointed out, refers only to the mental suppression of that which *is*).

" Existence is not a given, a pure received. . . . It is an active and effective presence; the body is the instrument of this presence which is presence to the self because it is presence to the world." [97] My body is the mediator because and to the extent that it is act, movement, gesture. From one side, it is an object located in my perspective; from the other, it is the center of perspective, the subject. It constitutes me as subject because it is a dynamic existence, not simply perceived or felt, but " self-moving."

Object insofar as it is objectified, subject insofar as it objectifies, the body brings about its own dualizing objectification. I am in the world and *I* am: the one is possible only in correlation with the other, and has meaning only through my quality as body-subject. " The self is for itself (*pour soi*) only in being for the world " is one way of expressing our mediating incarnation.

CHAPTER VI

The Body, Locus of Individualization and of Its Surpassing; the Relationship

I

OUR BODY IS NOT SIMPLY THE MEDIATOR OF OUR THOUGHT, THAT is, of our *humanity* itself. It outlines and hems in the inimitable individuality of each spirit, of each visage, circumscribing its personal singularity.

The profile of a face and the form of a hand; the expression of a smile or of a glance; the attitude and temperament of each person, and even his particular character, genius, and charm; the originality of his intellectual, ethical, social, and religious activity, which cannot be confused with that of any other person — all these traits are shaped by the body, in the actual change and mobility of a history.

This theme seems to be more limited and commonplace,[98] yet it will lead us to the heart of our study. How is this so?

I have pointed out the insufficiency of the spirit-body dualism: the body is (inhabited by) spirit. To say that it is (inhabited by) soul, that it is living and full of meaning, of projects, of practical possibilities, that it is "intentional," is not to emphasize enough the fact that the transcendence of a judgment of value, of meaning, or of truth, renders the body incomprehensibly *heterogeneous to itself,* both supernatural and natural. Reciprocally, I have also pointed out that this judgment of truth and this thought are gestural; without body, they would evaporate into empty abstraction. But we must go even farther into the concrete nature of this corporeality, of this reciprocal bestowal, of, so to speak, this reciprocal incarnation, and we will do so by revealing the individual marks and the palpable proofs of it in each of us.

When we say that the body bestows the historical and geographical originality of each person, as well as his psychological originality, we are obviously thinking of the unparalleled beauty of a mouth or a chin. Doubles are anomalous, and provoke laughter or revulsion in us. The stereotype is in " the body," not in " *our* body." The spectacle of two interchangeable identical twins, which adult life has not been able to differentiate, troubles me greatly. So, we allude to one's way of walking, and also, to be sure, of the originality of the artist; however, it has not been realized enough that our corporeality situates us in the here and now, without any alibi or excuse.

Thus the body takes on the significance of a veritable *engagement of the spirit*. It places me at the foot of a wall of a concrete situation unique in the world. In this situation it forces *me to reveal myself as I am and as I am worth*, in my relationships with men, in work and in play, in peace and war, security or danger, happiness or unhappiness, justice and injustice, health and sickness.

The body, in a word, is that which *individualizes*. This statement needs certain clarifications.

The idea of *individuality* is acquiring an increasingly obvious importance in the sciences, not only in biology but in physics also. Today we teach discontinuity in the very midst of the continuity of reality, the irreducibility of individual structures. In what we continue to call matter, we discover the existence of unities endowed with organization, stability, memory, autonomy, spontaneity, generation, and regeneration. We find individuality and finality in the atom as well as in the living embryo. " Thus, from the area in which mechanism and determinism seemed to have won their surest territory, we receive a lesson, namely, the fact of extraordinarily complex elementary existences (atoms), which are, however, stable and organized, with neatly defined boundaries, and which, far from being 'determined' by the environment, are endowed with their own life, spontaneously emitting unforeseeable packets of energy. Furthermore, they, themselves, are capable of reestablishing their menaced integrity, manifesting certain basic tendencies of the living being: perseverance in being, in its defense and regeneration, and even a certain autonomy of behavior which safeguards the secret of their resolutions. Continuity, organization, finality, autonomy, and, through the Spin, originality: are not these the major characteristics by which an authentic individuality is defined and affirmed? " [99]

Such is, indeed, the definition of individualization as we find it in physicochemistry, and as it is unambiguously asserted in life. But the individuality of which I wish to speak is not physical, nor even solely biological and psychological; it is global in the Aristotelian sense. I would especially like to emphasize that it brings up the idea of a situation of responsibility, of a certain perspective of judgment and of action. That is, it raises the idea of particular, precise, noninterchangeable points of view and of attack, or in other words, a position of work and even of combat.

When the moment comes to resolve on a decisive option, and even when the comprehension of a mathematical theorem is concerned, we know that the assistance of others has its limits (" No one can put himself in another's place "). In this respect it is not sufficient to speak of individual originality. The *hic et nunc* is expressed in terms of *situated* freedom and responsibility. The psychological characteristic is, here again, the sign of an ethical and spiritual reality.

The body places me in situation. It forbids me the general, the alibi of generalities. This is not simply conditioning, but a *task*, a *job*.

The body, then, is the organ of the differentiation of tasks and of the structuring of responsibilities. Just as my body structures time and space [100] according to existential coordinates that are my own and not those of others (*my* perspectives), so does it designate and define *my* task in the world. Everything, in each of us, is *oriented*, with a right and a left, because we are body, synchronized and coordinated. The body marks out the coordinates of the soul and of the spirit and synchronizes them to my responsibility. The body, in a word, is the spirit *in a person.*

It could be suggested that the body is the "finite" of the soul. It draws up the outlines, actualizes existence, and commissions certain things to the exclusion of others. How many possibilities are sacrificed in the course of man's life through this pitiless actualization! The body eliminates, *but only to elect.* It is the locus of the particular as against the general (but not as against the universal).

Consider, for example, friendship. The soul would love *all;* the body-soul loves with particularity, with all the negativity of an exclusivism. It is an *exclusive* friendship. It excludes as much as it elects, *but it does elect!* The body brings me to an election, to differences, to choice. It is yes or no; it is not yes-no.[101]

The body has a vulnerable opacity: its contours describe it and reveal it — naked of flesh. Compare to this the enviable and contemptible evasion of the "invisible man." No evasion is possible for the body. It forbids me to "shirk" and forces me to show myself, even in concealment and falsehood. It obliges me to throw off the mask.

For the body is both mask and description.[102] The body is precisely this concealing-revealing agent, this mask-mirror that betrays us despite, or more profoundly, through and by, our very concealment.

There is a revealing nakedness of a face (which explains in part the use of veils), of a gait, of writing, of a vague gesture: "It is indeed his." There is no way of passing for another, of being another. This was my dream during my adolescence, the age of revolt, of autoposition and opposition, the dualist

age par excellence, in which one discovers oneself in front of
the world and escapes from the world, the idealistic age, the
age of obliqueness and ubiquity.

But one soon learns humility: the feeling of humus, of the
earth. The body is the frankness of the spirit. When one has
a body, there is no way of "wriggling out of a difficulty," of
disappearing like a thief, of playing with or mystifying the
people surrounding, of using the alibi of the indefinite (as a
ghost slips away in blurred contours). With this humility, one
becomes less pleased with idealistic egotism. One no longer
refuses to participate in the debate, as it were (where it is
necessary to commence a debate).

No, we do not scorn the *materialism of the spirit,* nor the
materiality of the bread and wine. Religious sacraments rightly
aim to express this materiality of the spirit and this dignity of
matter inhabited by soul, that is, invested with meaning (this
dignity of the body as sign of the spirit).

There is a proudness in such a spiritual materialism that is
contrary to the denial of the spirit; there is a challenge, a
wager, an act of courage, an act of humility.

In order to be spirit, I do not have to disavow matter (which
is a created work). It is said that we descend, our spirit, into
matter, in order to become a living body, an incarnated spirit.
Evolution, it is true, makes possible a second reading of things.
In this sense, instead of descending, we would mount up from
matter through a disconcerting, incomprehensible, and mysterious process of "complexification," which puts the *more*
potentially in the lesser, like a giant tree in the seed (however, the bursting forth is more improbable, since it neces-
sitates the leap between nature and *repudiated* nature, i.e.,
supernature).

II

The incarnation of Christ serves as the preeminent illustra-
tion and revelation of the *dignity of the body,* the particularism of which he exacerbates, indeed, to the point of para-

dox, of harshness, of scandal. And how he does this! The Christ in this man, in a corner of Palestine, in a given year under the Roman occupation, in the midst of an insignificant people reduced to servitude! Why not elsewhere? Why not everywhere and at all times? The geographical and historical materialism adds its defiance to the materialism of the incarnation, against everything that we know of the universal nature of truth.

The fact is precisely that the mystery of bodily individuation, although it is set over against the indefiniteness of the yes-no, is not in opposition to the universal.

The already familiar theme of Personalism is that of emphasizing the perfecting of the universality of the person in singularity and diversity themselves. In respect to each one, the "reciprocity of consciousnesses" institutes a unity of another order. This unity is no longer that of a visible series, but that of love (invisible to eye, limited to appearance). The universal in the particular is, indeed, the miracle luminously brought to realization through love, as this thought of Jacques Paliard has admirably expressed: "The universality of love requires the singularity of souls."

It is necessary to ponder over the personalist paradox, which is reality itself: unity is not homogeneity. Nor does it correspond to an absence of individuality. On the contrary, it corresponds to the surpassing of individuality in a *relationship* of community and of communion.

Now, such a surpassing bases itself on individuality in order to accede to a pluri-individual or communal unity (or, in other terms, it bases itself on the individual in order to achieve the person). Such a surpassing, a reestablishment, is the very work of my corporeality, of my incarnation. The body, indeed, which individualizes me and centers me on myself, is that which permits me to surpass myself, which gives me the possibility, the occasion, and the mission of " decentering " myself.

Such is the magnificent work of germination and breaking forth of the body, of which I would like to speak.

Without my corporeality, would the word "surpass" have any meaning? And would the following exhortations have any meaning: liberate yourself from yourself, strip yourself in order to have access to an existence, a unity of a different order; get free from your "little self" and accede to the spirituality of the "forgetting of self." Are not all these appeals for surpassing and self-giving rooted in (in order to rise out of) the soil of individuality and even individualism, without which their impetus would slacken like a spring that has lost its elasticity?

Through my body I am centered; I am egoistic and world-devouring; I aspire to possess, attract, direct, and assimilate the different to myself, in order to transform it into my own substance. Ambition and gluttony are just so many aspects of the same biological avarice, which manifests itself as essentially possessive. The *individual* is he who proclaims his lust for power and for self-affirmation against and toward others. This lust bears a name and provides a philosophy: *individualism.* Nothing counts but me. Everything happens through me and for me. What will become of the universe when my consciousness dies? It will cease to be!

Well, then, this body, the center of interest and of interests, is somehow the soil or the substructure of my very disinterestedness. One more thing, if the body were not prone to monopolizing, what would it mean *to give oneself?* "Whoever would save his life will lose it"; all the "contradictions" of the gospel are what one finds posed and resolved in real life, through a dialectic of individuality and transindividuality at work in our body and in our flesh. Our corporeality alone is worth to us this risk, this honor, this occasion of fall or of salvation, this realization of the paradox.

This is an illuminating dialectic, if one considers in passing the relations that could not be ignored between *the great truths of the dualist ethic* (of which we spoke at the beginning of the book) on the one hand, and *the great truth of the incarnation,* on the other hand. Yes, the dualism of the Stoic type, and all the dualisms of defense, of combat, of mastery, of liberation, even of sacrifice and giving, can only be grounded on the "monist" soil of the body-spirit, from which they draw their strength and their existence (like Antaeus [103]) and without which they would lose all substance and all reason for being. The truth, and the very possibility of the dualism ethic, is the reality firmly centered in monist individuality, which furnishes the dualist ethic with this truth and possibility.

Let us open a second parenthesis. The individuality of the body-spirit, as we have stated previously, *creates* and *annuls* differences; it assimilates in itself that which is different from itself. But it reveals itself as the agent par excellence of differentiation and of heterogeneity. The high and the low, the more and the less, and, similarly, conflict and victory, effort, asceticism, obedience, extend me outside of the self and render me capable of delivering myself into other hands, that is, of *decentering* myself. All these movements, out of which arise new differences, are the work of the body. *One cannot decenter himself except through a centering.* One overcomes only a "here and now." There is no possibility of liberation except by and through this partial and exclusive individuality, through this "entire" body that judges everything from its concerns and points of view. The person is exactly this surpassed individual. It surpasses it because the person is rooted and incorporated in it.

The person, then, in the Hegelian sense, is the *negation* of the individual, of this individual whose body gives content to the assimilating *and* differentiating particularism. *At the moment of this "negation," the heoric dualism uproots me from my indissoluble individualistic unity, before being, in its turn, traversed in a postdualism* (of which we will say more later).

The negation of which we are speaking is dialectical; it signifies, in fact, a surpassing. This is why it is, indirectly, an affirmation of the body, and of the value and truth of the body, as a stage of its very surpassing. In order to surpass the body, it is necessary " to exist the body," to assume it. In order to accede to the spirit, it is necessary to adopt the incarnation. And one accedes to the spirit only in the incarnation.

Such is the movement and rhythm that lifts man out of what he is, that makes him both himself and other, nature and more than nature, the locus of immanence and transcendence. The surpassing of the dualist type transcends the individual in order to engender the person which, in turn, aims beyond dualism to the rediscovery of incarnation.

Thus the person is rooted dialectically in the body, in its beginning and in its end. It is united with the body through a triple bond of conditioning, structure, and negation, which we have considered successively. The body is at one and the same time condition, structure, and dialectical moment of the person.

III

A deeper analysis of the relations between the body and the person should lead us to a better understanding of exactly what we mean by "person," and what is meant by "Personalism." [104]

The person is the Nietzschean surmounted-individual; but this individual elevated to a higher power even now encompasses the ensemble of his relationships with others and with the world, relationships that are many-sided as well as being of horizontal and vertical dimensions. The individual opens, breaks forth as a seed, and becomes a tree, and becomes a forest. The person is the surmounted individual, but above all, the pluralized individual, the pleroma: *the person is several.*

The person envelops others in its very acceptance, through concern for others, through concern for its true (i.e., correct) relationships with others, and through love; and also through the reciprocity of relationships (not that it submits to these relationships, nor even that it simply accepts them: it assumes them, and requires that they be borne as a burden and as a symbol — as one assumes his responsibilities, or as one claims his place in the forefront of danger, his place of friendship and honor in the battle).

The person is several; this is what the dialectic of the body brings into view better. I want to try to explain this.

By taking support on the individual body in order to move out of it and go beyond it, the person, in fact, *transforms the significance of the word "body"*: it literally makes it break forth. It opens the individual to other persons. In becoming person, it becomes communal and accedes to the universal. This is what we mean by the change of "valency" of the word "body." This word thus takes on a transindividual meaning (one speaks, for example, of the "social body").

This is not at all a question of metaphorical or analogical language, nor of an imprecise meaning that ceases to have any meaning. What does "social body" mean, why "body," and what type of relations does it have with the individual body? Analogy is related to the idea of structure, of organization, of coherent unity possessing a certain finality; and we quite readily compare the social organism to the biological organism (its leader to the head, etc.). This scarcely presents any difficulty, but it does not sufficiently show *how* there comes about the change in meaning or valency of the word "body," of which the person has become the sign. In fact, we have bridged a chasm, and *the body has taken on a scope that seemingly denies the body.*

The social and cultural body *denies* the individual body in at least two ways.

Consider, first of all, that my hand is the limit of my body in only one way of looking at it. Instruments, tools, machines, radio waves, rockets and so forth, push back the limits of my physiological body. So, the first "breaking forth" is that of *the fact*. Bergson points out that perception is in all that we perceive, which places in opposition our immense real body and the miniscule apparent body. "People are never tired of saying that man is but a minute speck on the face of the earth, the earth a speck in the universe. Yet, even physically, man is far from merely occupying the tiny space allotted to him, and with which Pascal himself was content when he condemned the 'thinking reed' to be, materially, only a reed. For if our body is the matter to which our consciousness applies itself,[105] it is coextensive with our consciousness, it comprises all we perceive, it reaches to the stars. . . . We are really present in everything we perceive, although through ever varying parts of ourselves which are the abode of no more than potential actions." [106] The first, then, is the breaking forth of the fact.

The second is *the breaking forth of love,* which is no longer simply factual. It is a need and a choice (we will come to this again later), and, in other terms, the capacity of assuming *more* of the realities of the world, of enlarging to fit the dimensions of the world. I suffer along with my child, with my countryman, with the Algerian, with the Indian. There is a planetary influence of sympathy and of redress. This is the second breaking forth of the individual body.

This double breaking forth of the body (the one of fact, and the other of right or of choice) calls for two clarifications:

1. This breaking forth, which we have called " of the fact," must be somehow *reconciled,* reconciled to itself by the second (the breaking forth of consciousness and of love, which is capable of integrating the first into the body-subject). It must be recovered through an equivalent " distension" of consciousness and love. Otherwise this first breaking forth will produce only foreign and hostile instrument-objects, in which it will be alienated. Atoms and rockets turn against man; they alienate him, as we say nowadays. This is the tragedy of our time. It is obviously true regarding the atom. Yet it is equally the case regarding our chemical or other therapeutics, for our social welfare, for our progress, each on its own level. We deplore the fact that technology, having grown beyond all bounds, soon moves beyond man's control and threatens to crush him and annihilate him. We deplore the fact that man has become like a slave to technology. We deplore the fact that the worker is alienated by the product of his work, not

only by capitalistic subterfuge and diversion, but by the simple fact of becoming objectified in a product-object that already escapes his control. When we deplore all these things, we then become aware, properly, of this breaking forth *of fact* of the human body, a breaking forth that has not been recovered by a breaking forth of understanding and love.

This is explained by saying that the "moral sciences" have not kept up with the physical sciences. The individual body is constructed to expand, to break forth, to empty itself, to overflow into all parts, in proportion to the universe and to all men. But his head and his legs have not enlarged in harmonious proportions. The glutton's eyes are larger than his stomach. And so with modern man, his tools are larger than his heart. The adolescent who grows too fast is no longer properly proportioned. Man must be given time to recover his proper dimensions, to take stock of himself, to proportion the breaking forth of his body so that the breaking forth of justice might be adjusted to the breaking forth of atoms (that is, so that *choice* or *right* can be adjusted to the *fact*). To the degree that he can do this, he will cease to be alienated. He will be able to hope to reconcile himself to the self and to nature. He will thus become contemporaneous to himself.

Man's entire concern is thus to come to the point of *wishing* and of taking on that which happens to him *disproportionately* in relation to his former dimensions. The manual implement, for example, is charity from the rich to the poor. His business consists of making his responsibility equal to planetary and interplanetary dimensions, of recognizing himself in his own exploits, of wakening finally to his vocation "in the image of God" ("Fill the earth and subdue it").

2. Now, to place our second remark in perspective, the breaking forth of the individual body on the universal plan of the personal body is in constant danger of falling back into a "provincialistic" unity of a new order, into small circles that are nothing more than intermediate individualisms (for example, the individualism of the *couple* in sexuality, familial

and national egoism, the egoisms of classes and social levels, of races and continents, of religions and ideologies). The social body brings us at the same time to a breaking forth and a closing, a reclosing on the self, a falling back onto conquered territory.

Thus the social body becomes another individual body, a new organic and organized structure, a new centering, which requires in turn a new decentering, a new breaking forth. We can see why the term "social body" evokes not an opening or a progress, but rather, an order, a finite unity. This is the individualist snare of the social body. The sociologists, at least, seek a conciliation between opening and closing (as Bergson's two sources of morality and religion), between order and progress, evolution and *revolution*.

Love gives us a perfect example of this double movement, inspiratory-expiratory, of centering and decentering, which belongs to the body-spirit. There is a possessive love and a giving love, a self-seeking love and a charitable love. All forms of furor and of peace are found in this *rhythm of corporeality*, which is the rhythm of our respiration itself. Those acquainted with the nature of biological rythms admit that there no longer exists a symbolic analogy between the double movement of respiration, on the one hand, and the double movement of centering and decentering, on the other, through which our individual body becomes, through multiple enlargements, the personal body with the dimensions of the universe.

Such a correlation of biological rhythms and sociocultural rhythms should not be astonishing, if we understand the body as the mediator between the abstract elements of human dualism, and if we understand the body in its *expressive* function as well as in its potential of promoting cultural and spiritual attitudes. It does this in our respiration, and even more in our way of moving or of extending our hand. These things *express* the dimensions of our body. Yet respiration also affords, being itself a corporal-spiritual rhythm (or just corporal, in the proper sense of the term), the impulse of our cultural and spiritual rhythms. Our respiration (its modalities, the position of its maximum amplitude) not only expresses our whole personality, but in returning it exercises on the personality a beneficial or harmful induction. Thus, anything affecting one, affects the other as well. This is, moreover, what the sages of the Far East have fathomed in their experiences with yoga. It is important to learn how to respire in order to learn how to live.

We have talked about the successive breaking forths and the imprisonments, the openings and closings, which lead the individual body to the *universal body*. The universal *denies* the singular only in the sense that it causes it to blossom, fulfills it, and increases it in an infinite network of love. God is indissolubly infinite and personal, transcendent and present in this created world. The incarnation of Christ gives us the key to the paradoxical unity of the universal and the particular. Christ sums up in his body all the meanings of the word "body." He is the *name* of the mediation of the universal in the particular, the name of the relationship of a transcendent God in the very midst of human relationships. Paul says to "yield your bodies . . . as implements for doing right" (Rom. 6:13, NEB), that is, as implements for true and authentic relationships between men. The mediation of transcendence is verified in these relationships of right, without which the meaning of transcendence would slip into any number of evasions related to the occult possession of esoteric knowledge. The mediation of transcendence is justice, which is verified in body-person to body-person relationships: "I was hungry, I was thirsty, I was sick, I was in prison" (Matthew). The touchstone of the love of the transcendent God ("Love God with all your strength") is confirmed in men. And the relationship of justice between men bears the name of Christ as its true name.

When I say that my individual body breaks forth as a seed in the fulfillment of the personal body, I mean that I bring to realization this body of relationships of justice (universal); I enter into the body of Christ. We are, to use a wonderfully suggestive language, the very body of Christ. This means: *my true body is the world,* woven of relationships between men of flesh.

Now, as I pointed out previously, I feel that the basic pivot is situated in this: the successive breaking forths of the individual body into the personal body are not only, and cannot be contented with being, facts of pure ascertainment. They are related to a need and a choice on our part. It is a conscious choice, or a lived choice. Thus we can state that *it is in his body that man will be judged.* In other words, he will be judged according to the *significance* that his body has for him, or, to put it another way, according to his *attitude* regarding his body. Or to put it in still another manner, he will be judged according to the *dimensions* of his body, according to its potential for cooperation and love.

The second part of the book will examine this passing of our factual corporeality into the choice of our incarnation.

CHAPTER VII

The Meaning, or Dimension, of the Body

I

OUR ATTITUDE REGARDING THE BODY, THE MEANING OF OUR BODY, the dimensions of our body: these are three expressions of one and the same choice, which determines our status as persons.

Does my body possess a reality other than that which my attitude toward it confers on it? [107] Does it have a reality other than its meaning for me? When all is said and done, we have the body that we *merit*, the body that we are fitted for.

This is why I said that the body-object is the body *objectified*, that is, in some way *chosen* as object; and the body-subject means the body *chosen* as subject. The body-object and the body-subject express respectively a body assumed or non-assumed by me. It is an either-or proposition: either the body will be completely taken in charge, *chosen* by the incarnated spirit, or, on the contrary, my body will be, for me, this limited reality that my spirit does not integrate (the cuticle or the skin of the spirit, or, as Bergson said, that part of the spirit which has fallen back into matter, has precipitated, has solidified).

The truth which hopefully will come out of my account is that our attitude regarding our body, thus polarly schematized, *reflects and expresses our attitude regarding the entire world,* and that, in and through our bodies we ultimately witness to that which we are and to that which we want in our most profound verity. It is in and through my body that I bear witness. It is through the body that one sees the man.

There is what I would call a *depreciatory idealism of the body* that is strangely confused with a depreciatory idealism of the *human condition* in general. We all know this from experience, and we all have lived it at certain times in our life, in the adolescence of our life (there are some who remain adolescents all their lives).

An essential moment of our progressive maturation toward adulthood is characterized by an ensemble of reactions: the rejection of bodily and social conditioning, which is more than a contempt of conformity; the search for a surrealist escapism that shatters the structure of the body as well as cultural structures; a curious and paradoxical mixture of iconoclastic detestation and of idolatry of the body and of the human condition.

As an adolescent rebels violently against his parents and his environment, as a new people reveals itself aggressively nationalistic (which is quite understandable), so does this idealism of which I am speaking affirm the spirit only in reaction to and disparagement of the body and the human condition. It affirms the *I* only in conflict with and resentment against the world. Idealism and solipsism are combined in affirmation of absolute and theoretical freedom, sometimes to the extreme of theoretical suicide (in the manner of the Kirillovian nihilists [108]). Nothing is of significance to me, nothing exists but me, nothing exists in me but the spirit, which repudiates all shackles. Now, he who denies the universe in order to exist will, in turn, consider himself as the world in his own bodily existence. His exclusive affirmation of self ends by excluding himself from his affirmation. It is one and the same thing to deny the universe and to deny oneself as body, as an existent in the universe. *For the body is the symbol of the human condition.*

Our civilization is presently in the adolescent stage of un-satisfied technical exuberance. It is in the uncertain, inter-mediate, ambiguous stage of the disparagement-idolatry of the body (i.e., of the human condition). In the final analysis, dis-paragement and idolatry of the body are the same thing. But how is this so?

For some, the technical idolatry is combined with a disem-bodying and dehumanizing idealism, which aims to subdue animal conditioning and, in place of the real body, to substi-tute another entirely synthetic body born of electronic genius. The superman of Nietzsche was a hero; ours is a robot. Lunar rockets and test-tube babies and the dictatorship of man by robots are combined with Huxley's "best of worlds" in the dreams of our modern neurotics.

For others, this same technolatry, far from being disem-bodied in the coldness of the laboratory, is admirably suited to a certain frenetic materialism that scorns spiritual values and aids the seductions, pleasures, and frenzied immediacies of the body (consider, for example, certain modern dances, which only superficially achieve the spirit of African dances). Ado-lescence has two faces, especially when it is forty years old.

This possibility of the perfectly contradictory interpretation of the individual's attitude as well as of the mentality of our adolescent civilization, seems to me to be understandable when one becomes aware of the *profound complicity that ob-tains between the contempt for the body and idolatry of the body.*

Contempt and idolatry are two forms of materialism or of idealism (which come down to the same thing), for both have restricted our body to the petty limits of the individual body.[109] Both make the body fall back to the level of the body-object. The idolatry of the body, in fact, has made it an idol-body, which is a body-object, since it is not *recovered* in a signifi-cant or, if I dare say so, a sacramental intention. This idolatry of the body limits it to the individual body by excluding or being ignorant of the surrounding world into which the body is incorporated. Inversely, idealism, which turns away from the body, succeeds only in completing the same negative and nihilistic operation. The two misappreciate the body by seeing in it only a body, which is adored by one and abhorred by the other.

On the contrary, this same body, when it is *recovered* in a meaningful intention, then responds at one and the same time to two interdependent operations: (1) of the negation (surpassing) of the body-object or idol; (2) of the breaking forth of the individual body into a world.

The affirmation of the body-subject and the affirmation of the world body (that of human relationships, the Christic body) are really one and the same affirmation.

Our technical civilization participates, then, contradictorily and simultaneously in an idolatry of the body and in a disrespect for the body. Materialism and idealism, these hostile brothers, are more similar to each other than we think. They characterize the dualist or *critical* moment of our development. Now, we must undoubtedly come to this critical moment, but we must also go beyond it in order to reach a " new childhood." This new childhood will not be precritical, but *postcritical*. It will rediscover the salt of the earth, the communion of things, and something like the flavor of our body, namely, the absurd privilege of our corporeality and our incarnation.

When idealism yields to the disincarnational current, it does not take account of the extent to which its scorn for materialism is materialistic, since it treats as material a body that is not such.

But idealism will understand this later, when, as a prodigal son, it returns to this house, to this body which is the house and native country of the spirit, of which a diabolical angelism meant to deprive it. Yet for the present this idealism indicts our body with all the resignations of the spirit, as one shifts the guilt to a scapegoat. In a cowardly manner, it accuses the body and escapes. It is like a hit-and-run driver, and leaves the scene of the accident.

Idealism is Manichaean. It makes the body the *locus* of egoism, so as to reserve for the spirit the privilege of interaction and love. But the truth is, however, that as body-spirit *we make an unambiguous choice*, for egoism or for love. As body-spirit, we remain entirely enclosed within ourselves or we turn fully open to the world of men. We are completely *flesh* or spirit.

The Pauline term "flesh" expresses something quite different from a topography or an anatomy. It expresses the orientation of the whole man, of his spirit, that is, the spirit in which he lives and which will manifest itself either as anti-Spirit spirit or as spirit that is docile to the Spirit.

This is what I attempted to express previously in saying that our body is the locus of our individuation *and* of its surpassing. In reality, it is as *incarnated* beings that we are either *flesh* (individual) or spirit (person). We are soul-body for better or for worse, for spirit or for flesh. And it is in the body that we will be judged.

The dividing line is not located between the body and the soul, as is too often believed. Rather, it comes between the flesh and the spirit, which is quite a different thing. For it does not involve "regions" of man, but rather, an attitude and a fundamental choice of man. The opposition resides in the choice that I have made, and not in the parts of which I am composed in the eyes of abstract analysis (body, soul).

Certain "spiritualists" have only disdain for "materialism," without realizing that true "materialism" (in the pejorative sense) does not come from matter, but from the spirit that rejects it as such, that is, from this dualist spirit that engenders, at the same time the two symmetrical twins idealism and materialism. Both harmonize in the same "materialism" of matter.[110] The true distinction lies elsewhere: it is in my attitude, my spirit, my total orientation that I reveal myself as "materialist" (i.e., *individualist* and narcissistic — and how many idealists are materialists in this respect) or "spiritualist," to use customary terminology (by "spiritualist" is meant, turned toward men, open to right relationships between men, in other words, *person*).

These contradistinctions of various formulas are not blind windows. They are intended to reveal the extent to which my body is wrapped in my choice, the extent to which my attitude regarding the body (which is an unavoidable dualist way of expressing it) furnishes the characteristic manifestation of this *choice*. One cannot conclude a "spiritualist" pact with the spirit by scorning and hating the body or by rejecting it as an encumbering object. On the contrary, this is an attitude of flight, a disguised or unconscious materialism.

In a word, it is absolutely necessary to overcome the Manichaean dualism that would place *body-egoism-individual* on one side and *spirit-love-person* on the other side. This is an error of perspective, and how illusory and dangerous it is for the health of man and of the world! Man is *one*, for better or for worse, for the flesh or for the spirit, for death or for life. And it is our corporeality that makes us workers for salvation or for anti-salvation, for our freedom or for our alienation. " Man is saved with his body and not from it." [111]

II

Our thought should be of great value to us in the elaboration of an *ethic of sickness*, as well as in an approach to a comprehension and an ethic of *sexuality*.

Instead of thinking naïvely, and, as it were, *topographically*: the *body* or *sex* is *here, spirit* is *there*, is it not necessary to try to understand that there are two global attitudes in which I completely participate, as body-soul-spirit? There are two perspectives, two choices, two ways of living sex, the body, and sickness itself.

To say of sex, for example, that it is animal, or anti-spirit, or materialistic,[112] is simply to express our refusal to assume it, our conscious or unconscious intention to empty it of spirit and separate it from us. Our epithet is intended to qualify sex, when in reality it is we whom it qualifies.

For our way of meeting it changes and witnesses to what we want to make of it. The body and sex are not *objects* that could be qualified from outside, as chemical objects. And this is not even exact in physicochemistry, where we are told that the observer is implied in the observed, which is never neuter, the observer-observed couple constituting an indivisible whole. This is even more true of our body: to maintain that the body is paired with the spirit is to separate it from the spirit. This is nothing more or less than evincing a separatist choice, a true segregation and true racism of the body!

Thus we have two ways available to us of considering and living our body, our sex, our sickness. There is a separatist way, which evicts the body and sex from their proper abode. A racialist or, if I dare say so, an ecclesiastic stance is taken toward the body and sex; they are denied the legitimate birthright of participating in the spiritual life; they are defrauded of this divine birthright, which is truly a denial of justice. The second way, on the contrary, accepts them and permits them to remain in their abode, which is our abode; they are recognized as identical with us as subjects and are integrated into our personality.

It indeed involves a conscious or lived choice. It is indeed a matter of an attitude and of a spiritual state, of a mentality on our part. It is in no way a matter of an objective, ascertained fact, of which we would only have to make note. *We are entirely the architects of this artificial materialization of the body and of sex* (the latter sums up the problem in its most critical area). It is similar to a situation in which certain bourgeois persons confront lower-class people: both are ill at ease, yet proud at the same time. They are afraid of each other and each expresses in his own way his inability to integrate the presence of the other. The same is true of the individual confronting his sex or his body. Not having integrated it, he changes it into a foreign body, an instrument of subservience and of alienation, a "wrapping."

Body and soul [113] are thus authentic *partes extra partes*, through this refusal or inability to integrate. (I have discussed this elsewhere in regard to the ideas of necessity and of evil.[114]) It is a matter of concepts and proof, which are signs of an attitude of noncooperation and noncollaboration with the whole of the creation. These are not objective realities, but the results of a particular intentionality, of a biased and partial orientation of our attention.

Thus the idealist (or the materialist, or the dualist) attitude regarding my body, or my sex, or my sickness, manifests itself as an attitude of *non*cooperation, of *dis*engagement, of resignation, of the intellectual withdrawal into the shelter of what we describe softly as " our interior life." It is like the individual who tells us: " Politics do not interest me; it isn't my field of competence. I pay no attention to what is happening in Alabama (for example). I have enough to do with my family, my profession, my ' speciality.' Everything else — I don't want to know anything about it! " This is the attitude not of the *person,* but of the individual (in his little corner).

The *world* and, similarly, my *body* " are of no concern to me." This is what is implicit in the foregoing attitude. For it is obvious that the attitude that turns me away from one, turns me away from the other. It keeps me from assuming the body, even if I appear to be occupied only with it and idolize it (we have emphasized this previously).

But is this a valid comparison? And, also, do we not encounter daily men and women who are " committed," as we say, and who give themselves completely to various causes of the world, all the while neglecting unbelievably the appearance and maintenance of their bodies?

Indeed, we must guard against two false comparisons. The first makes a comparison between those " authentic secularists " [115] who have forgotten their bodies and the imitators of *The Imitation of Christ,* who have abandoned both body and world.[116]

The second would place opposite and compare, as if they

matched, the "culture" (physical or sensual) of the body and an engagement in the world, which is something different from an idolatry. One can be committed to the world, as one can be committed to the body, in a spirit of service or in a spirit of servitude. The two senses of "self-giving" should not be confused (the prostitute gives her body and the soldier gives himself). There are certain "givings" that are really "takings."

The truth is that whereas the one has quite well managed the distinction between the two ways of giving oneself to the world (one for service, the other to be served), the other (which hinders hygiene in asceticism) maintains a distressing tendency to confuse the *care* of the body (which is a respect for the creature and for the Creator) with the *idolatry* of the body (which is a caricature of them).

This is what makes us sad when we come into contact with certain people, laymen as well as monks or nuns, who are devoted entirely to the world's needs (without being of the world). Not only do they neglect the elegance, suppleness, and beauty of their muscles and organs, but they also succeed in compromising their health, their effectiveness, and their strength in the service of the work undertaken. We see these devoted ruins wearily dragging themselves along, fat or pale and emaciated, without muscles, never having seen the utility of physical exercise, or the need of proper respiration, suppleness, of keeping "in shape."

These people are "short-winded" in the service of others, but at the cost of a self-contempt that includes their bodies. Without judging the merits, of course, I do think that these men and women present a spectacle that is not very edifying, the spectacle of an imbalance in the order of efficacity and in the order of truth.

I am thinking also of another error, the paradoxical nature of which we formerly acclaimed, namely, the idea that genius and "madness" go hand in hand, as if the latter could exalt the former, when in reality it thwarts it and enfeebles it. Another mistake is that nervous and busy activism, that feverish

hurry of certain good men who put themselves at the service
of all types of action committees, and who finally end in being
unable to perform any real activity. There are so many dispro-
portionate and vicious attitudes, which resemble the abomina-
tions of certain " child prodigies." [117]

It is my opinion, then, that holiness does not have the right
to be disinterested in health, and that the service of the body
is a necessary form of service to others. Egoism, like altruism,
can be lodged in the care and (or) the refusal of the body, in
the care and (or) the refusal of the world. The distinction lies
in thinking of one's body and of the world in terms of *responsibility.*

If it is true, in fact, that the idea of responsibility means that
I am affected, in varying degrees and priorities, by the totality
of the body of the world, and if it is true that it is precisely
this awareness of the body in the larger sense (the body woven
of relationships) which constitutes me as a person, then all
idealism-segregation of the body is a refusal to assume by personal responsibility in the world.

It is, in other words, a refusal to assume completely my condition as incarnated being. That means that the same attitude
of cooperation which forbids me to divorce myself from my
corporeality, forbids me to withdraw from the world. It means
that the one is the other, that my body is the world (the world
is the political and religious dimension of the body). And this
is not a statement of fact, but a requirement, a right, a spirit, a
choice.

It is I who, through the meaning that I am able to give to my
body, my sex, or illness, shrink them to the dimensions of the
anatomical body, of the body-object, or enlarge them to the dimensions of the creation, of the body of Christ.

My body has the dimensions of my spirit: it is that which my
spirit makes of it. And according to whether my spirit (my
mentality, my intention) is " materialist " or, on the contrary,
docile to the Spirit, my body in turn is itself matter or
spirit.

My body has the dimensions of my spirit; my humanity is taken in charge through my body. It is my body that makes me present to the world and to men; it is the potential of presence. Is it not through the body that we fail or succeed in our task in this world? The body impedes and limits, but at the same time favors communication and presence. It fulfills justice or injustice, thus obeying our fundamental choice. My body indeed represents the geometric locus, as it were, of this choice. I mean by this that it is the most evident test of my fundamental attitude in my physical, familial, professional, social, cultural, and religious life.

I insist strongly on this alternative, which is inscribed in an antidualist and *antitopographical* logic: body and spirit are in no wise two *regions* of man, but two *possibilities* of man, who is body-spirit (in one single word). There are two possible attitudes, which are precisely that of the individual and that of the person.

My body is spirit. One could say, in other terms, that it forms a zone taken in charge by the Spirit, in an operation consisting of assuming and irrigating the greatest number of zones of the universe, thus restoring them to the vitality of the Spirit. This operation consists of enlarging my body to the dimensions of the world (as Bergson says of memory, which enlarges time and space; the soul defines itself through its power of extending beyond the body in all parts [118]). But if we go beyond a dualism of the soul and the biological body, then, indeed, my body is not this physical and psychical body arrested in its pattern and project. It extends beyond itself in all parts; it is project, creation, and life, through the species, through civilization, through culture. My body is spirit, the zone irrigated by the Spirit. And this taking in charge does not stop after having made a good beginning; it enlarges in concentric circles, like a rock tossed into a lake, to the ends of the universe.

The taking in charge of my corporeality begins the taking in charge of the entire world; it involves the same movement, the same fundamental choice on my part. It is the political choice of justice among men, the religious choice of resurrection of men.

Thus the idea of my body enlarges in proportion to the progress of my taking in charge of the world, in proportion to my capacity for assuming, for sympathy, for dialogue, that is, in proportion to my love. And it should not be surprising that I add here the properly religious aspect of this consecration of the dignity and worth of the body; the idea of the body finds its ultimate in that of the body of Christ.

We must understand the Personalist and Christian paradox, which proclaims both the infinite worth of the particular body (in the dogma of the resurrection) and the sole reality of the universal body (in Christ).

The person both affirms the worth of the body and denies its ultimacy. This is only an apparent contradiction. It enables us to avoid confusing the anatomical body (body-object), the body with freckles and stomach ulcers (Is it not ridiculous to hope for or imagine the resurrection of this body as such?), with the body-subject, the body as meaningful structure, in which these same characteristics and these same maladies are *reassumed* and become *signs*. They become *sacraments of our own incarnation;* in short, they cease to be individual and become personal.

It remains for me to explain what I mean by the body as the sacrament of our incarnation.

CHAPTER VIII
Sickness as Sign

I

MY BODY IS PERSONALIZED BY ME, REASSUMED IN AN INTENTION that makes it *the sign of what I am.* My body is a sign. It is the sign and decisive test, the touchstone, the meaningful proof of that of which I am able to show myself worthy and capable. It is to my body that I will reveal what I want and what I am worth, i.e., *that which I am.*

It is in this test of the body that I will give evidence of my docility to the Spirit or of my rebellion against the Spirit. We say that the body is given to us in some way as a *sacrament.* But in the idea of sacrament or sign, we must include the idea of a charge that is confided to us. Our body is the sign of this charge, which is to fulfill for the glory of God one's earthly condition as " creature-creator " consecrated through his work to the domination of the world and to right relationships between creatures. One's *incarnated* condition is his condition as person.

II

I think it important to dwell somewhat on the idea of work and to show how the mediation by the body is incarnated and is surpassed in work; how my corporeality is expressed and perfected in work, the transformer of the world and the realizer of right and true relationships between men.

A. In work, we see too exclusively the sweat and the utility, the yield and the profit, the negative and hostile aspect of it, its mercantile aspect as the means of achieving pleasure and comfort. The metaphysical value of work is discovered more profoundly, in the vocation of our humanity, which is to humanize the universe, in the vocation of our liberating freedom, which cooperates in the heart of a creation that is in the process of eventual maturation and fulfillment. This latter is, if you will, the objective, historical, cosmic, and eschatological pole of the metaphysical meaning of work.

But the other pole interests me even more. This pole concerns our own transformation as workers, our fulfillment, our humanization, and our divinization through work, which is the body of our bodies.

For, as my body brings my spirit to *realization* and puts it to the test of life (as iron is tempered by the test of fire), so does work test my body in its dimensions as tool, as machine, as invention, as technical. My body inserts me into the world; my work inserts me into the world twice, as it were. It multiplies, extends, consolidates, and confirms this insertion, this commitment, this marriage, this "bear hug" of the world. It creates the object, the *Work* (*Oeuvre*).

As a disembodied thought evaporates into an "ownerless phantom," so with an intention that does not become embodied in an action, so with a man who does not confirm his incarnation in work.

The world becomes my body through the mediation of work, which roots me in the world. This recuperation and incorporation of the world into my body corresponds to that enlargement of the body to the dimensions of the world that I discussed in the preceding chapter. They meet each other. Yes, through my work the world becomes my body, through a kind of assimilation comparable to that of a nourishment. And, inversely, this work manifests to the world the verity of my body.

How does work become the verity of my body? Without it, my body would deny itself and repudiate itself in an escape from life, in an escape from incarnation. It would repudiate its love for life. It would deny that life is love. For work reveals the idea of the transformation of the world, through the effective realization of this idea. And this idea of the transformation of the world is the soul and goal of all love. Work is concrete love; not simply the intention, but the effectualization. This means that love, as with responsibility, can have only a real and material content: work. Our daily choice, which gives meaning to our lives, is daily minted, distributed, and completed through work.

B. As the transformer of the world and the realizer of civilization, of political and economic structures, work provides the basis for my real relationships with men. It forms the environment and the means for grasping the value of *justice*, which is itself the postulate (in the Kantian sense) of true relationships with others. In short, work provides me with the concrete test of character of my corporeality, of its substance and depth of reality, of its human potential (not only its industrial and industrious potential), of its potential for justice, that is, for love. Work is of the expanded body, of the " en-loved " body, as it were. If my body is my sign, this sign is signified by work, which becomes the sign of this sign which is my body.

But if this sign has been well understood, we would be wrong to look no farther than to the literal aspect of this world-transfigurating work, since this transfiguration has no meaning in itself except through the relationship and the love of which it is the goal. This relationship and love then locate work in what could be called a " beyond of work," from which work would take both its meaning and its strength.

Work (and the body and, indeed, all things) is itself only in that which is more and other than itself, that is, located in a " beyond " of self. Every reality receives meaning only in situating itself in a reality that registers it and confers upon it its correct place. Work is thus registered, and profiled, as it

were, by a "beyond" of work. I mean that it is not self-suffi-
cient, that it neither finds in itself nor puts on its aim or its
raison d'être. Work is restored only in "denying" itself, in going beyond itself, as I pointed out concerning the body, of
which work, once again, is the sign.

Thus one perceives the meaning of *sickness,* this scandal and
mystery that interrupts the fulfillment of man in the creation.
Sickness, old age, and death together outline the contours of
this space beyond work; indeed, they make work meaningful,
and put it (or put it again) in the service of a reality that
goes beyond it.

Thus there is a dialectic of work and of the "denial" of
work. This reminds me of a passage from Abbé Lochet, which
is quoted with justifiable approval by Gabriel Marcel: "Who,
then, will make this technician sense . . . that to identify man
with his work is to bind him to a task in which he loses himself, is to turn him into an instrument of production, a thing
to be used and, in the final analysis, an earthly damned? Who,
then, if not one only: the sick person. We can get rid of the
dead person. But the sick person, what do we do with him? He
is no longer good for anything, and if he can no longer be
useful for production, it is necessary to make him disappear in
the world of tomorrow. This is only normal. . . . But at the
moment of striking the sick person, the worker stops short. . . .
There is a mystery here. The sick person is no longer a worker,
but he is still a man. . . . He is loved even more in his impotence and infirmity. Why? What is it, then, that must be
recognized in him? It is not his money, for he is poor. It is not
his capacity for work, for he is incurable. But it is the man
himself, . . . the man who goes beyond the earth and all that
it produces, . . . the man who is the image of God." [119]

The feeling of *uselessness,* in sick people themselves, is very
revealing both of the central place of work and of its insufficiency. It forces them to understand a beyond of work, that is,
its full significance that forbids us to confuse it with production. This beyond of work reveals that the transformation of

the world is more radical and more unlimited (so to speak) than that which is immediately understandable on the level of work reduced to its literal dimensions.

The sick person "invites us to thoughtfulness" (Claudel), or more exactly, to hope, that is, to a total reading of reality. In the midst of a society that is ready to canonize expansion, production, and yield, here we have the scandal of the sick person, who comes to impose a beyond of work in order to put work in its proper place. And the sick person, in turn, barring a sinking into his impotence (in the limited order of potentialities of transformation), learns that potentialities of transformation provide only a participation in the infinite potentiality of divine love to which they are ultimately related and from which they receive their very strength. Work is the servant of the beyond of work, in which is inscribed the mark of its success or failure in the here and now, in which is inscribed its goal of justice and the failure of this justice. This justice always regards the beyond, pants after it, fails, and dies through the sickness of the body (a provisional dualism), but the undertaking is pursued in the beyond of the visible body or the body-object, until the glorious body, the body-subject, is realized. And the beyond of work reveals, finally, that it is the entire humanity, in the body, which is transformed, and not solely my partial and provisional individuality: all work is social, but also social is the meaning of failure, of uselessness, of impotence, of sickness, of death, in a suffering and triumphant communion that we call the communion of saints and that manifests the initiative in us of the love of God. The Absolute is engaged, in fact, through an initiative that is world-transforming love (*agapē*), and this initiative is located in our work itself, which is the body of love. Thus transcendence becomes an active and transforming intimity in us. This is why work, the visible body of the world-transforming divine love, the witness to this love in the world, does not receive its meaning from itself, but is grounded in this beyond which is the very love of God for his creation.

III

Sickness is presented, then, in counterpoint to work, as a major sign of the global test of our incarnation: *it is the sign of the sign which is the body*. By that I mean that it is this sign carried out to its maximum of feeling. As physicians we ourselves must understand and bring our patients to understand not only the meaning of sickness but also *that sickness is a sign*.

Sickness is the sign of that which we are, but it is this in two ways. It is important to make these ways more precise.

The one *reduces* us to what we are (and nothing more); the other *calls* us to what we are (and nothing less).

My sickness, in reality, defines and qualifies me first of all as a nonresolved problem: in this sense, it marks, as it were, my insufficiency, or again, if one wants to go farther and to speak in figurative terms, it marks my " sin." [120]

But, at the same time, my sickness marks me as a test, as a type of election that befalls me, a distinction and almost an honor. What will I do in the face of sickness? How will I behave? It is like a wrestler whom the crowd awaits excitedly and anxiously. He is expected to demonstrate his worth and also his philosophy of life, his hidden virtues, his unknown resources, in short, he is expected to reveal himself.

Sickness is ambiguous; it is the sign both of my problems and of my resources. It allows itself to be interpreted sometimes as a resignation, sometimes as an assuming, for it is the occasion of both.

When one wonders, in the presence of a human conduct, or more especially of a conduct of the body, of a sickness: " What does it mean? " (or what does it have to tell us?) one can wonder, in reality, of what chink in my armor, of what blemish, of what secret failure this conduct or this sickness is the sign and the witness for the prosecution. Sickness delivers me up naked, manifesting a childhood deprived of love, a maturation poorly achieved. A sickness betrays the conflicts that it endeavors to resolve.

But in the face of this same conduct, of this sickness, I can also wonder what need, what vocation, what health, finally, it witnesses to (in an upside-down fashion, as it were). Of what health or of what spiritual aspiration does it outline the traces, the psychological signature? And especially, of what psychological ascent does it give the alarm and divulge the secret?

Yes, our acts and our sicknesses, in short, our bodies, *express* us. They express both what we have not taken care to be, and what we take care to receive from them.

We will always discover these two visages, these two possible interpretations in an act, a conduct, a belief, or a sickness. The one interpretation is "retrospective" and the other is "prospective." The one diagnoses what I am, in the sense that I am nothing other than the "only" of a pure statement of fact. The other begins with the "only" of this statement, and extrapolates the vital prolongation. In other words, it indicates what I am *beyond* pure facticity.

My sickness expresses such a "beyond": that which I am and that which I am not, or rather, that which I am already on the mode of not being (yet). In short, sickness expresses, in its way, how I aspire to become what I am.

Social events, the dreams of individuals, and our illnesses themselves express, to be sure, profound and repressed desires. But they also express the profound meaning of these desires, of these repressions, of these failures, and of this goal to which they witness, to which they are implicitly related. The "only" contains a reference to an aspiration, to a vocation, to which failure or sickness witnesses in its upside-down language (failure or sickness witness as such and because of what they are).

My lacks indicate both *that I lack* and *what I lack* (in reference to which one can speak of lacking); lack, illusion, failure, and sickness can be produced only in relation to a full reality. Infirmity points to this reality that we call plenitude, without which we could have no test of infirmity. Similarly, injustice *points to* justice, the permanent reference. The potential of being sick, as that of being sinner or fallen, is possible only for those beings having a vocation for health, for salvation, for blessedness, for natural and supernatural health.

Our body, and more decisively and acutely, our sick body, expresses our problems, but also our resources: it expresses our theoretical and practical resources, that is to say, not only the vocation to which they bear witness, but especially the vocation that they actualize, that they catalyze, by serving as the diastase of this actualization, and by furnishing the occasion of a success through failure itself and through sickness.

Sickness reveals that which we are in fact and that which we are capable of being, i.e., our *nature* and our *verity* (in the double acceptation of these two terms).

A wound in my physical or psychological body permits my difficulties, my conflicts, my unresolved complexes to show through. It reveals that which I am, my nature and my verity, which is hidden behind the flattering mask of a social and superficial pretense, a pretense of sociality, or of health, a pretense of steadiness or of success. Psychoanalysis brings out these depths of truth, behind a sickness as behind a skill, a love, a marked taste for archaeology or for athletics, a scruple of conscience, a subtlety of opinion. When someone has shown his cowardice at a crucial moment, we say that his true nature is revealed. Indeed, through this sickness that has, so to speak, broken loose from me, that has come out of me despite myself, that I submit to while at the same time it seems that I commit, I have revealed my nature, my verity, in the retrospective or negative sense of an " only " (i.e., that which I am, no more and no less, that which I have not known not to be).

But our slips, our dreams, our lacks, and our sicknesses express our *nature* and our *verity* in another sense: *that of which* I dream, *that which* I lack, *that toward which* I am directed, are expressed as a vocation and a goal, not only by allusion and indirectly, but as a calling to fulfill myself through the symptom or the trial. My nature leads me toward my nature, and my verity illuminates my other verity. All my actions precede me and follow me; they present two faces, expressing my initial verity and my terminal verity, the two poles of *my* personality and of *our* humanity.

My sickness reveals to me the way in which I behave toward it, in which I utilize it, assume it, surmount it, transform it, and incorporate it into my verity. It is a conditioning, but also a testimony, a recapitulation, but also an ambition. Without it, I could not have discovered that to which I could aspire, that to which I was called; I could not have realized that which it alone has enabled me to fulfill, namely, an unsuspected destiny.

Deficiency is always a want in reference to a fullness, and when I become aware of this deficiency as such, I am called to a fulfillment.

Sickness prevents me from being comfortable. It is the school of *poverty*, in every sense of the word, and especially in the sense of poverty as enriching. Suzanne Fouché [121] has pointed out the degree to which the body of the invalid is the place of unexpected victories, of discoveries, and of new resources, of which the man who enjoys the use of all his limbs and all his possibilities can have no idea. The operations that remain possible to me with what is left of a paralyzed arm, or a reduced respiration, or an almost absolute immobility, become an adventure and an exploration and bring extreme joys. Not only energy, but activity and results as well, are increased tenfold, to such an extent that it becomes possible for a maiming to promote a superior technical and social qualification. Suzanne Fouché has devoted her attention to this favorable result, which raises the level of a life above that which it had been without the sickness. No one is better able than she to express the nature of sickness as a " promotion," the gain contained in a loss, the *more* contained in a *less*, the *resources* where others would see a *problem*.

IV

By now someone will perhaps be saying: " I first came up against amoebas when I was eight years old. But I see no resemblance between that event and the description you have given of a sickness as the sign of what we are, of our destiny and of our vocation."

Have I, indeed, forgotten sickness as encounter? Sickness happens to us. It falls upon us, as the enemy or the highwayman. It is obvious that it does not come from us, that it comes, indeed, rushes at us. Its determinism is external. In no way does it manifest the man who I am, except *afterward*, in the use that I make of it, in the advantage that I will be able to draw from it. In this sense, we can say that sickness is a sign. It is a sign that is addressed to us perhaps to see what we will do with it, to see, indeed, what manner of men we are. Sickness as encounter does not contradict sickness as test. It is sent, as Job's sores, to test man's faithfulness as servant of God. I do not at all forget the power of sickness as encounter, which teaches us better than anything the " power of the times of sickness," the " proper use " of sicknesses. This latter does not consist solely of meeting the crisis with coolness and clarity, with humility also, and with dignity, with patience and with hope; it consists primarily of seeing in the crisis a message of God, his way of beckoning to us.

Sickness as accident and sickness as test constitute two faces of one and the same conception (let us say, " external ") of sickness. In this sense, sickness is brute facticity, the unforeseeable irreducibility of an encounter, a rupture with what we were. It is a brute, unique, irreducible existential moment.

How do we discover the relationship between sickness as encounter and sickness as sign (which I seemed to be generalizing about)?

One way of answering this question is to say that there are sicknesses as accidents and sicknesses as signs, and they are not the same. I have made such distinctions, as does everyone, between the " external factors " and the " internal factors " of sickness and healing (cf. *La Guérison,* Chs. II and III). On one side we find the accident, the injury, the microbe; on the other we find the terrain of the sickness, with its aptitudes and liabilities. The encounter corresponds to the aggressive sicknesses; to the terrain, the sickness as sign. This is obvious.

It would be obvious, indeed, if these two species of sickness could be neatly divided into opposing camps. But I mentioned only the external and internal *factors:* both are operative in the same sickness, which is then, at one and the same time, encounter and sign. For example, an industrial injury is a sign of an intimate conflict in my life, either temporary or permanent (as is well illustrated by the case of " accident-prone " people). Another example, the aggression of microbes, which is apparently the most fortuitous occurrence (poliomyelitis, amoebic dysentery, etc.), is evidence of a deficiency of terrain (which explains, moreover, why the aggressors attack me, me among others, and at one particular time rather than another). To be sure, at the extreme one can refer to sickness as encounter in its brute state: mass airplane accident, mass food poisoning in a restaurant. The *collective* clearly indicates that these things do not involve me personally (in our sense). In these events the sickness could in no way signify the man who I am. It is purely extrinsic and limited. Yet even in this respect certain qualifications and attenuatings are necessary. The very havocs provoked by the accident will bring into play the suppleness and the resistance of some (there are some, in parachuting for example, who know how to land, and some who do not know how to), the awkward tautness of others; and this will be brought into play at the very moment of the encounter, of the confronting of the chute or the dangerous item of food. Finally, at the risk of falling into a discussion of fate, the simple fact of finding me in a given airplane on a given day, or of being seated before a given meal, is, despite all, something dependent on me, and not on pure and simple chance. I am the man who has " exposed " myself to this meal, to this trip, or whatever, through my chosen profession, through my taste for travel, or my aversion to remaining home.

Perhaps some will think that I am pressing the case for the idea of sickness as sign a little too far, but my intention is simply to show that the external and internal factors are not mutually exclusive, that they are intimately mixed in every sickness, up to and including terminal cases. This permits us to replace the idea of a division into two types of sickness with the idea of a distinction between two conceptions of sickness.

" But, rather than two types of sicknesses, is it not necessary to see, in such an opposition, two possible ways of fighting against *sickness,* of acting against the aggressor or the organ, or, on the contrary, of acting against the terrain? Or perhaps it would be better to speak of two ways of healing, two points of view, two possible perspectives on the sick person, two fashions of understanding the same reality. Organic illness and functional illness (in our terminology, sickness-as-encounter and sickness-as-sign) are less two types of sickness than two ways of conceiving of sickness. One is organicist, and localizing or materializing the suffering as much as possible; the other, which is structuralist and functional, aims at grasping man in his totality and in his comportment. Thus they are two methods. An element of reality (morbid) comes to bring confirmation to both. Certain sicknesses, certain sick people, certain patients lend themselves better to technical medicine; others are more comfortable with the medicine of the total man." [122]

Indeed, certain sicknesses lend themselves better to the idea of sickness-as-sign, others to that of sickness-as-encounter; but there is present in all sicknesses, more or less, something that permits them to be viewed in one way or the other. And one will always oscillate between the monist and the dualist definitions of sickness.[123]

Undoubtedly, the present-day trend and fashion incline us to overestimate the terrain, the personal conflict, the sickness-as-sign. In the heart of a dialectic between facticity and freedom (the former favoring sickness-as-encounter, the latter favoring sickness-as-sign), Sartre, for example, has maintained that nothing happens to me that is not intentional on my part: I behave in such and such a way *in order that* something will happen to me.

We would express ourself in this same dialectic by setting into opposition, as it were, a Kierkegaardian conception of sickness-as-encounter and a Hegelian view of sickness-as-sign. The Hegelian view locates each event of reality as a necessary moment-sign of my history, of our history. The Kierkegaardian view, on the contrary, emphasizes quite radically the irreducible nature of the encounter, of the rupture, of the leap, of discontinuity between that which I am and that which happens to me, and that with which I collide on my way. It is the thunderclap, the conversion of Paul, reversal, drama. The same event, which strikes one as a thunderclap, for another (perhaps a better analyst) will unveil his prolegomena, his secret presemeiology.[124] There is the thunderclap only for the impassioned blind person. Kierkegaard showed himself quite perspicacious concerning his own case, his own moment. Hegel, after having passed through this phase of the existential encounter, analyzes the encounter insofar as it is sign. The existential absolute, unique, unforeseeable, accident, sickness, thus discovers its true visage: a moment of my history, a sign of my history.

Let us remark that the dialectic of the Hegelian type manifests sickness-as-sign under the visage of determinism or of fate, whereas the Sartrian existentialists make it a sign of our freedom, in that we have contributed to the happening of whatever happens to us. In this perspective, the affliction to which we submit would always be, to a certain degree, an affliction committed by us (so to speak). We would always be accomplices in our misfortune. For the Sartrians, the encounter would be the sign of our facticity; for a Kierkegaardian, on the contrary, it would be the sign of our freedom. This opposition between the two "schools" of existentialism is more apparent than real, for the accident-facticity provides the occasion of our freedom, of the liberating action, and thus we are the architects of our destiny for both perspectives. Freedom and facticity are intimately and inextricably combined, but to the advantage of freedom.

Would not medical empiricism be shocked by these philosophical considerations? It seems to me that our practice intersects with our reflections, and that it gains depth and assurance from them. Without becoming involved in superfluous theories, it is of advantage to always remember that in each encounter there is a sign to be perceived, that is, we read in it our visage and our path.

I realize that some readers would remind me of the point made before, namely, that the individual is the accomplice in, and to a degree guilty of his illnesses.

The reader, if he has not already "become guilty," so to speak, should not fear that he will be rendered guilty. Taking into account the definitions made in the first chapter, I would recall that the absolute rule of the physician is to avoid judging. And if we call this rule *neutrality*, the physician is absolutely neutral in *method* and in *spirit*. In the daily exercise of his profession, and in personal consultations with his patient, the physician maintains a *suspension* of all value judgments. However, this professional blind spot does not, of course, hinder his judgment *as man*, nor his reflections on the possible relations between, for example, sickness and "sin."

The physician finds himself confronting either *sicknesses lived as sin*, or sickness that seems to be tied, directly or indirectly, to a "poor moral attitude" (greed, resentment, pride, etc.). The physician's task is not to judge, but to receive and welcome the patient's becoming aware of his sickness-lived-as-sign and to heal him, that is, to liberate him. He does this either by elucidating with the patient his unhealthy guilt feelings, or by helping the patient to get out of the mental rut that influences him in an unhealthy way.

Whether sickness be a sign on the subjective, existential mode (sign-for-the-patient), or a sign on the objective mode (symptom-for-the-physician), in any case it yields my true visage, the man who I am, including the significant fact that I live it (sickness) as a sign. A sickness resembles my fingerprints that I could modify: sickness serves to find or to lose my "trial" in the dynamic mobility of a history over which I have some control. A case of poliomyelitis is a sign of my psychobiological history and of some of my problems. I am able, however, to be ignorant of this; indeed, one can never know it objectively. In this sense, sickness will be a sign only for a subject, a subjective sign, not an objective symptom; it is not a symptom, and always a symbol. The physician and the patient have to reckon with this sign lived as such.

In the presence of a sickness lived on the mode of sin (the behavior of guiltiness), let no one bring up to me the "neutrality" of the psychoanalyst who says (and I have some examples): "Sin does not exist!" Behind this *imaginary* guiltiness there is, perhaps, a truly defective moral conduct [125] (the case is similar to the flippancy with which "hypochondriacs" are treated, which is a strange way to become acquainted with them and to heal them). We must not throw out the baby with the bath water. To render guiltless as a group and without discernment would not be beneficial for a sick man, who would, as I have said, replace concern with "offense" with a concern for imaginary offense ("not serious"), and would be afflicted, to boot, with a type of infirmity. A therapeutic exculpation that leaves a void behind it ("sin does not exist") would have fulfilled only half its task, taking the easy way out. But more important, it would not have *respected* the person of the patient. A prudent elucidation, which respects the signs lived by the patient, not only permits him to rise to the level of his problems and to become aware of his problems, but it also does not stop at the point of a complete blank, with all guiltiness swept away; it exercises, and helps to practice, the virtue of discernment. It is necessary for the patient to leave the petty stage of "imaginary guiltiness," and to say, "This is what my offense comes down to, such as I have been able to disengage it from its unhealthy matrix," or perhaps, " Here is my offense, such as it is forgiven."

In short, the evacuation of the guiltiness-sickness (or sickness lived as sin), if it leaves only a void, has not been neutral, has not respected the man. It has "assumed" even more about the man, perhaps, than if it had dared to judge him.

I have spoken, and we have the right to speak, only of sickness *lived as sin*. I have not spoken of the real relations between sickness and sin because I know nothing about them, since sin is outside of the bounds of my judgment as physician or as psychologist. Sin, or even offense, is not located on the same level as the clinical statement.[126] The two could not meet.

We often hear that saints have a certain tranquillity, whereas sin makes the rest of us fret and worry. Or, on the contrary, we are told of the sufferings, sicknesses, and neuroses that seem so often to be the lot of the best and most saintly people. But I am not certain that in this respect we have not confused the spiritual with the psychological, that we have not mistaken one for the other, or have embodied one in the other. The virtue that brings happiness, the prayer that invigorates, and so forth, belong to the order of hygiene, of the technique of life, of psychology. Sin and offense, on the other hand, belong to a different order. They are no longer of the order of fact, but of judgment. And judgment does not belong to our world.

This is why sickness-as-sign can in no wise be taken in the absolute sense of a physical symbol marking out my relationship to the universe; rather, it must be understood in the sense of a sign lived as such on the personal and interpersonal level.

V

Sickness expresses our problems and our resources, the two meanings of our nature and of our verity. But these resources, this nature, and this verity, which show us what we are and what we have chosen to be, can teach us a lesson if we are attentive. That is, they must be translated into a theoretical language, which is that of a doctrine, of an ethic, or of a spirituality of sickness. Such a spirituality or ethic comes *afterward* in order to explain an attitude that is lived. Otherwise, the doctrine would be only abstract chattering. One does not squander theoretical suggestions on a patient; he has better things to do, and so do we. Nor does one impose an ethic of sickness, especially when one is not sick himself. All that one can do is to try to translate the example or the specimen.

The sick person can either indulge himself in his sickness, or he can become set against it. Or else he can commit himself to and become reconciled with his sickness in the very battle that he wages against it. The same is true in this respect as is true in all forms of warfare, in heroic, knightly, gallant man-to-man combat, or in the total warfare that sows devastation and uprooting, in the warfare that observes the rules, and in the warfare that transgresses them. So with sickness: there are some who play the game, and others who refuse to play, openly or slyly, with fury, artifice, or despair.

We notice two phenomena in our patients. In some there is a more or less conscious docility and servility regarding the sickness. In others there are manifest imprudences, for example, in the overworked persons who go beyond the instructions of the most elementary regimen of relaxation, in order to resume their four hundred mile circuit on the roads. Cowardice and defiance are inverse forms of hostility, and both externalize an aggressiveness toward the self, toward the world, and toward God.

An ethic of sickness could, then, become hardened in the stage of a heroic dualism, which, as I pointed out at the beginning of the book, arises directly from the pathological rupture itself. The noble Stoic ataraxy gives an exact replica of the body-as-enemy-of-sickness. But Stoic dualism, which prescribes detachment from the body, rediscovers reconciliation with it through the detour of a pantheistic monism that locates the individual in the destiny of the universe. To speak of thoroughgoing dualism is to betray, in part, the essence of Stoicism, just

as vulgar epicureanism misrepresents Epicurus. I want simply
to point out that the resources of man can be mobilized in
force against sickness and the body, just as they can be mobilized in duplicity and betrayal. Thus, in a war, subversion
and espionage carry on their underground game, covered by
the noise of arms. Using sickness as a ruse can be a conscious
tactic, but it is more especially an unconscious strategy, which
psychoanalysis unmasks and transforms. The things that are
concealed in the initial sickness become perseverations in sickness. He who "presents" (to use Balint's term) a case of migraine or colitis is sick from not being able to put up with his
mother-in-law or his professional responsibilities. He uses
trickery against an abnormal situation and projects it onto an
organic symptom that is easier to identify and handle: the organ becomes the memory aid (or rather, the aid for forgetting),
the true sickness, the true pathological problem.

Thus an ethic of sickness can go no farther than this stage
of a dualism of overt or covert opposition, of conscious or hidden opposition. But an ethic raised to the hope of redemption
goes beyond the dualist stage of the body-object, the tricked
or mastered enemy, and ends finally in *reconciliation with the
body.*

VI

At the critical moment of the sickness we will declare a lived
choice rather than a deliberated choice. It is a global and lived
choice that sums up my whole life, of which the sickness serves
only to illustrate the mood, the style, the spirit.

This observation will assist us in trying to conceive, if ever
so little, how the obscure meaning of the sick body constitutes,
for the very young child and for the old person, a choice and
the evidence of a choice.

What meaning can the body of the sick child assume for
him? Dr. Pierre Robert has spoken of the meaning of the
body for the child.[127] In detailing the different phases of de-

velopment, the "successive puberties," and the dynamic principles that regulate bodily rhythms, he invites us to make a distinction regarding the body *of the child*.

This point of view avoids the perilous attempt to break open the subjectivity and the intimity of another person, and of another as different from the learned adult as is the infant or even the older child. The study of the meaning of the body *of* the child utilizes terms that are objective; it measures weight and size, it describes behavior, morphological signs of individuality, development, crises and attachments, dullness and slowness.

The meaning of the body *for* the child requires a different type of boldness and risk and perhaps an inadmissible boldness. In fact, the risk is twofold: (1) of falling unwittingly into objective descriptions and classifications; (2) of gratuitously imagining an interiority of the infant beyond his behavior, without any more justification than the analogous attempts of descriptions in animals.

In the extreme, it involves a wager; I must move outside of my adult psychology, beyond the bounds of intersubjectivity, and sympathetically match my consciousness to the dimensions of the child's nonreflective consciousness.

For example, when the psychologist tries to grasp the appearance in the child of the body image, he runs into the same two risks that I have just mentioned. There is the risk of objective notation: "At one month, the baby recognizes his mother; at three months he discovers his hand; at eight he acquires the idea of unity and of bilaterality of the body." Do not these impassioned precisions of Gesel [128] jump the wall of objectivity? The baby is described in terms of attitudinal reflexes, of the conquest of vertical planes, of different postures, of equilibrium, orientation in space, etc. This is a space of hearing and a space of sight, and the senses play a primary role in the child's acquisition of awareness of his body. For example, by touching himself, he gains the idea of limits to the surface of his body.

Also objective, and of great import, is the idea of "dis-rhythm" which is suspected as being at the origin of illnesses and of the distress felt by the child. "Disrhythms precede by several years the first indications of settled illnesses, as they are described in medical journals. The development of rhythms in the course of the duration dominates psychology and medicine, which become rhythmologies of different na-tures." [129]

A step toward an appreciation of the *interior* of the sick child's consciousness of the body would perhaps be furnished by the idea of anxiety, which certain scholars trace back to the traumatism of birth and which is aggravated by the potential states of asphyxia of the newly born: "The very young child," writes Robert (*op. cit.*), "experiences anxiety and pain, but I do not think he suffers as does the adult. It is his parents who suffer for him."

This is an essential observation, which should make us pause for a moment. It seems difficult to go very far in the interpreta-tion of the body *for* the child without closely associating with this interpretation the persons who surround the child with their presence and their care. And when we speak of a *chosen* meaning, it is indispensable to locate this choice in the *en-vironment* (not indistinct, but joint) that is formed by the parents and children in the family, or in which the child is placed in the hospital. Even more, this choice in each child is that of the entire civilization that has nourished him with his mother's milk.

I would say that the child's choice of the meaning of his illness should be understood in the same way as the choice expressed in baptism. The adults seemingly choose in place and on behalf of the child. They promise for him, and they promise on a plane of reality that goes beyond the order of time and of the empirical awareness. This is what is misunderstood by those who criticize the practice of infant baptism as an abusive assuming of the future. This act has the value of a symbol. We are not able to discern the intra- or intersubjective limits of it. The symbol is an "inner-outer" thing that is both subjective and objective.

Thus the atmosphere of the family or of the hospital, which saturates the clear-obscure consciousness of the sick child, truly induces his choice of the meaning of his body. His choice of accepting or rejecting his afflicted and painful body is reflected in trust, unconcern, anxiety, refusal, or obedience, rigidity or suppleness, cooperation or opposition in his very organs. And in this global choice, those around the child have unknowingly committed their philosophy of life and of death.

It is quite true that we all play a great part (parents, physicians, nurses) in the child's taking-in-charge of his illness, of his infirmity, in short, of his body. His "inferiority," his withdrawal, his flight, the duration and seriousness of his lesion and its consequences themselves on his social behavior with his playmates, his slowness or progress in school, all depend on the choice of "his" adults. A specialist in epilepsy would confirm me regarding the degree to which the social behavior of epileptic children results less from their attacks than from the catastrophic opinion that their parents have of such attacks.

Also, the meaning of the body for the child is not limited to its individuality nor to its interiority: the meaning *is* the relationship to affection or neglect, to anxiety or trust in his entourage. It *is* the meaning itself of this infant body for this entourage. It is a meaning woven of relationships, completely symbolic.

Consider, for example, the child whose cancerous leg has been amputated: the future is summed up for him in this mechanical plaything, in his bed, in a space with particular colors and dimensions in which he has reorganized his outlook. We are astonished at his contradictory cheerful unconcern and his sober courage, at his perceptive intuition of his situation expressed in a strangely mature repartee that scares us. Or there is the child who suppresses, who "clams up"; there is the child who is one big complaint and magnified attention. In such cases there is a confusion of body and soul, a compacting of being in which there exist neither high nor low, neither right nor left, neither today nor tomorrow: but there is the maternal hand, immediate help, appeal, response. The child is only thirst, only nausea, in a concentrated body, a compacting to the extreme, as if to brace against pain and agony and to enter entirely into this pain and agony. This, and more, is read or hidden behind the silence and the frightful inertia of the very sick but seemingly tranquil little body; a moment of abatement, the sickness leaves the body tranquil, the child does not want to eat or to play; if he is left alone, he asks for nothing, awaiting a new pain when it will return.

The child expresses himself more by his look than by words. His games and sketches sometimes help us to better pierce the mystery of the meaning of his body. Each of the figures innocently traced on a piece of paper is a symbolic language that the psychologist learns to read and that reveals to him the infantile soul, that is, his body.

VII

We would think, perhaps, that the old person is less closed, easier to read (in fact, too easy in his prolixity). The child remains a secret, but the old person willingly talks about his dissipated body. Yet it is the muteness of old people that speaks volumes about them, that is heavy with meaning; and we know nothing at all of that which remains unexpressed behind the complaints or the gruesome whims.

Here again, we make use of an objective method (psycho-sociological and psychobiological); in our day gerontology is acquiring the importance of an autonomous discipline with ever increasing works and publications.

In our Western societies, the old person considers himself, and is considered by society, as a useless and unproductive body, in the charge of others. We emphasize the decrepitude of the body, this rag that forsakes me, this arm that can no longer defend me, this memory that leaves me. Seen by himself and by us, the two portraits of the old person differ from and resemble each other; they have influence on each other; they tell the story of a society.

Von Dürckheim (*op. cit.*) has studied old age in the light of Oriental civilizations: in the Orient the old person is convinced, in a society that consecrates and fosters this idea, that he comes to a crowning of life, to his fulfillment. Among us, in a world " exclusively tied to *performance* " (von Dürckheim), to production, doing, knowing, the problem consists above all of *not growing old* (he climbs mountains at seventy years!), and (or) of how to assure the subsistence of old people (charitable houses and works, to take care of the aged, to permit them to spend the remainder of their life without too much boredom and misery, to cheat time, to occupy among themselves these interminable and futile days). In the West, the body of the old person is a burden for society, for his family (" It is now my sister's time to take me into her home! "), and, finally, for himself.

But the bio-psycho-sociological approach gives us only indirectly the meaning of the body *for* the old person. The most striking thing, in listening to them, is their willing resignation. (" I'm no longer nimble; I'm twenty years too old.") In a word, they express their impotent bitterness regarding the body that they have become. Their bodies are unrecognizable to themselves, yet familiar to the point of being weary of feeling them in their carcasses. The most strange, the most unbelievable object is this conspicuous thing that clings to my wrinkled skin like my most intimate friend. It is no doubt the same with any disaster when it overtakes us: alien, yet very close to us; we find ourselves face-to-face with the immediately accepted inacceptable. How can one not accept that which *is?* And this thing which is ineluctably written in the ruins of my members, irreversibly. It is a loss that one can hardly be unmindful of or retrieve; old age comes to us and follows us slowly, completely unlike sudden misfortunes. We adapt ourselves to it without doubting it, yet all the while not believing in it.

Such is the meaning of the body that watches itself growing old in a civilization for which the major concern is to refuse to accept old age. Not to grow old, or to let oneself go: thinness or obesity show us the incidences of the state of the body on its own meaning for the aging person, and vice versa.

But the old person who learns how to say yes to his transformation ceases to frown in " a general attitude in contradiction to the cycles of life " (Dürckheim). He knows to surrender that which leaves him, and not to cease becoming new in an accession that no longer resides in a " producing," but in the order of " being there," in the inclination for the correct attitude. To put oneself in harmony with the future, to be attuned to the variations of one's body, to be in order, that is the secret of the meaning of the body, not so much for the old person proudly hale and hearty, capable of the performances of the young man, but for the old person in communion with his very weakness, which brings him a maturity and a peace.

It cannot be doubted that such an interior promotion of the aged body sums up an entire life and an entire civilization. The meaning of the diminished body constitutes a *choice* in a very broad sense, one which encompasses and sums up a life, but which also engages a human solidarity that we can only call the communion of the saints. In a very concrete sense, I and everyone in his job are responsible for the life and the approaching death of this blind and bedridden old person, whose earthly future is occluded, but who sees rising a " superterrestrial aurora " transcending time and the individual in his small body, in his " small life." The meaning of the body for the old person has passed completely over into another body; it is preserved only in being transmitted, only in giving itself and being increased; only in quitting, in short, the body-object, so as to strain more and more toward the realization of the personal body, which is *many* and spread throughout the earth and throughout all time.

VIII

Such, then, is this bodily, sick, aging, and mortal condition that is mine and ours, that I might and we might *together witness* to the life that is given us, that we might fulfill our task and show that of which we are capable *together,* our capacity for cooperation, for assumption, for obedience.

This is understood for each one in particular, but especially for *humanity in its wholeness, which forms one sole body.* The correlations between my vocation and the universal vocation, between my individual body that believes, suffers, dies and is reborn, on the one hand, and the growth of the world, the revolutions of the universe and the destiny, or rather, the design written into the creation, on the other hand, are recounted on innumerable records and with innumerable overtones in the symbols and myths of human language.

Our personal body designates our place in the Work (*Oeuvre*). A construction superintendent places one worker here, another there. In the same way, my body is given to me as a place of work, as the sign of the special type of service that I have to perform. My body plants me like a tree in my temporal and mortal soil, the child of God for the work of the resurrection, that is, of the gathering in blessedness. My body is not something that enables me to be contented with the negative role as the *sine qua non* condition of my existence and my work here below; it is more, it is *positively the major test of my humanity, of my humanization.*

Tell me your relationship to your body, tell me the dimensions of your body, and I will tell you who you are. It is in one's manner of carrying high one's body and of boldly taking on one's incarnation that one will see the man and that he will be judged.

It is in my body that I am seen at work: " I was hungry, . . . I was thirsty, . . . I was a stranger . . . naked . . . sick . . . prisoner " (Matt. 25:35-36). All escape from the body is falsehood. I work or I fall short in my body, in my earthly and human condition, in my body and in that of men, in my human body which is interdependent with other men in one sole body. It is in our bodies that I am false to us or that I deliver us and that I show " what I have in me," as the saying goes.

It is there that people expect something from us, and that God expects something from us. I am either an individual closed in myself, or a person participating in the creation, and it is true in sex, sickness, health, work, culture. For it is easy to " swallow " everything in talk: in my body, and thanks to my corporeality, I witness in *acts*. Hegel said that the act is the verity of the intention. No deceit is possible: " I was hungry, I was thirsty "; the body is given to us in such a way that a straightforward response is required.

Sickness, as the touchstone of this touchstone which is our body, reveals us as we are in the depths of our choice. It *reactivates*, as it were, the sacramental wound that is given to us, as circumcision or tonsure consecrates a vocation to the service of the Lord.

IX

Death is even more decisive than sickness. It is the sickness of the sickness of the body, the bodily condition carried out to the third power. It defines the decisive and culminating point of the bodily condition.

The definition of the incarnated being is that he is mortal. *Death is our sign*, because it is itself the sign of our body, which is our sign. It is not, however, the sign of the vanity of life, but the sign of the " straightforwardness " of which I spoke: it is the crucial sign of what is required of us, of what is made known to us, of the function that is marked out for us. It is the sign of that which we are capable of, the sign of what we are and of what we are not, since we must become and reveal what we are. Finally, it is the sign that God addresses to us, namely, of having to conquer that which we are. The symbol of the body is enlarged through a question-and-answer process in which we are not alone. A multidimensional dialogue is started, whose appeals seem to come to us from the world of the living and from " another world." And it is this same appeal, and this same response, of which death gives us only a hint. Death is the *sign* of several doors, but it itself is little revealing.

Death is our summary. In fact, it is impossible to speak of the person's attitude toward his body without speaking of his death. But although death is the sign par excellence of this sign which is our body, this discreet sign speaks a language that is ambiguous, obscure, hidden, and of several meanings. The most saintly persons can go astray through their manner of dying, of " muffing " their passage in this world. Reread, for example, Georges Bernanos and Graham Greene.

Furthermore, we are deceived if we read the body only in the first or second reading, that is, as covering, in the moment or in the appearance, as the reason for, or instrument of, glory, courage, or heroism, in other words, if we read it on the scale of and in the perspective of men. There is no doubt that in such a reading, the brain that betrays or that blasphemes, together with our cowardice in the face of agony and our shame in our weakened body, all contribute to confine us in a literal dualism.

But our witness through our body, in the third or in the seventy-seventh reading, Péguy would say, can break forth without paradox in the misery and shame itself of the body, which has become the eminent sign of our poverty and our humility, of the nothing that we are in the hands of God, all of which comes through him. In this way, we do not take refuge in the dualism of the body-as-betrayer; we go forward in the joy of not denying, but rather, on the contrary, of drawing near to ourselves, of embracing and espousing our very condition, which has been given to us as a difficult and unique risk in our statures as creatures made in the image of the Creator. One recognizes the artisan in the difficulty of the task.

The dying person has both a pitiable body and a splendid body; the pitiable body, as much and more than the splendid body, witnesses in three ways: first of all, it witnesses to our poverty, and to the extreme richness of this poverty; secondly, it witnesses to the exceptional favor given to us, namely, grace, of which this poverty attests. But the body also witnesses to our verity before the Creator, in the context of our entire life and in the context of our entire humanity, that is, of the communion of saints.

X

Our body is a sign that God gives to us. It is a language of God, by which he makes known to us what he expects from our cooperation in the Work.

Our body, its glories and its miseries, its sicknesses and its thousand deaths, is the language that we speak to God and to men; but it is also the language that God addresses to us through our humanity. Our body is his message. This is why I am able to say that my body is confided to me as a sacrament, if we understand sacrament as a visible or material sign expressing the presence of God in us, of that which he gives us and of that which he asks of us.[130]

Our body is the message of the living God. This is made more evident still through the incarnation of his Son and the primary sacraments of his flesh and of his blood. It is a message that we must know how to read, to which we must know how to respond. There is no better way to respond to this message than by our test, by our responsibility regarding our body and that of others, regarding our illnesses and those of others, regarding our death and their deaths.

There is no better way to understand that our body is a sacrament, a language between Creator and creature (a language moving from God to me, from me to God), than by means of the signs or symbols of sickness and death, which are not at all simply symbols of frailty, but rather, symbols of conquest, stages of fulfillment. We understand this even better, if possible, and exemplarily, in the suffering and death of Christ, stages of his resurrection. His bodily defeat and death, his death that was a death reserved for the rejected of the world, are stages in his reign and in his universal jurisdiction. The incarnation of the Son, his suffering and death, illustrate preeminently that our body is a sign, the sign of the Spirit and of our incarnation.

Both the incarnation of Christ and our incarnation are equally signs and a language, in inverse ways, so to speak; they come together. On the one hand, my incarnation is the act through which I assume and take in charge my corporeality; it gives meaning to my body. On the other hand, it is a response to the incarnation of Christ, who comes to meet me.

His incarnation is presented as the perfect *model* of my response itself, which mounts toward it, the perfect model of my effort to assume my corporeality; it is also the very movement of God coming to me to aid me, to call me, to lift me up to him. Christ puts on our corporeality in a divine pedagogy; he descends to us in order for us to mount up in him. Thus God gives us the gift of the very need he has of us.

Such seems to us to be the relationship of the two incarnations, the human that is modeled on and comes together with the divine. There is no comparison between their natures, yet they both speak the same language, which is that of the body. And they both have the same intention, which is the resurrection and the glorification of the body.

PRACTICAL CONCLUSION:

Respect for the Body

I

IF THE ORIENTATION OF OUR STUDY HAS BEEN WELL UNDERSTOOD, it will be seen that the body is *more* than the body. In other words, when one speaks of the body, one says more about it, in the final analysis, than is immediately evident.

A double lesson can be gained from this general conclusion (this double lesson is a single one insofar as it concerns physicians and present or potential patients): the physician should be *more* than a physician, and the patient and his illness should be *more* and something other than a patient and than an illness.

The physician will be more than a physician, or else he will betray in himself *both* the physician *and* the man. I have elaborated on this remark elsewhere, and will not develop it here.[131] I would, however, like to deal in more detail with this same need as it concerns the patient. His illness is something other and more than an illness, in the sense that it is the locus of a choice, of a meaningful conduct, of a fidelity and a witnessing.

The illness is a choice in two ways: choice is involved both in its etiology and in its intended purpose or utilization. It is a choice in the problems that find an outlet in it and that are expressed through it; it is a choice in the way in which it is, in turn, integrated by me into my personality.

Illness contains and confers a meaning that goes beyond it. If it is only an illness for me, it doubly kills me. If, on the contrary, it becomes the occasion of an act of getting hold of myself as well as for an act of surrender (conflict and obedience at one and the same time), then it doubly saves me.

I have attempted elsewhere to explain the false dichotomy, in sickness, of acceptance and of conflict.[132] This dichotomy is expressed as follows: pain should be combatted as much as one can; when there is no more chance of winning, it is to be accepted (as a kind of trial or mysterious good).

Thus we operate, too often, on two levels. But pain cannot play inverse roles, as it were. It cannot play a biologically useful role as an alarm signal serving life, while at the same time playing what is, in sum, a spiritual role, that of a trial which must be overcome or, if necessary, "accepted" when it gets the better of a person or when it turns against life. It is not possible to employ pain in a spiritual meaning when and because it has failed in its biological use, nor can one make a virtue of a deficiency.

This same "operating on two levels" is found on the spiritual plane itself, when we are told at one time that pain must be surmounted at any cost, at another time that it must be accepted.

Thus we see this type of tripartite, abstract, frightful, and false division to which we are brought. In the first place, there is a *portion* of pain that is understood as an arm of the living (thus, far from regretting it, we must respect it and praise it); secondly, there is a portion that must be destroyed as a harmful beast; finally, there is a third portion (the "remainder," as it were, that could not otherwise be "accommodated") to which one must become reconciled as a trial because it is obvious that one cannot otherwise bring anything meaningful out of it.

Now, this frightful division disappears when pain itself is understood and reinstated as a *sign*. Here it is the same pain that I meet in combat and that I undertake to battle. But the rules are those of individual combat, which have no comparison to the rules of total warfare. It is the type of combat celebrated in the *chansons de gest*. I esteem the opponent and I battle him. It is the same enemy whom I love and have a stranglehold on. But in this case I do more than accept the enemy by holding him at the end of my sword. I go beyond this dualism of grandeur, and the mortal combat becomes an identification or a marriage. It becomes a means of assuming a charge, of bearing a burden proudly, without submitting.

Each person can make this an act of pride and human self-sufficiency: " I shall bear (my deed) on my shoulders as a carrier at a ferry carries the traveler to the farther bank," says Orestes in Sartre's *The Flies*. " And when I have brought it to the farther bank I shall take stock of it. The heavier it is to carry, the better pleased I shall be; for that burden is my freedom." [133] Thus can one speak also of the slavery of sickness: my sickness is my freedom.

For the Christian it is that and more. The charge that I bear is in the likeness and example of God himself, who has desired to bear it for us in his Son. In his example, and bearing it with him, our pride is double, and is increased doubly by love. We must share his burden, which is our own and which is borne for us.

Thus the conflict becomes a form of love. Conflict can be an aspect and a major aspect (undoubtedly the proudest) of *obedience* (in that there is a way of challenging and rejecting the order received, which constitutes a form of homage to the authority of him who gives the order: a whole ethic of insubordination, as a form of obedience, is contained in the foregoing remark). And obedience, in turn, if it is not a fearful and cowardly resignation (i.e., false obedience), is sometimes found in conflict to reveal its true face (cf. the story of Jacob's conflict with the angel).

The understanding and reinstating of sickness as sign, in one sole movement, overcomes the meager dualism of acceptance and conflict (of acceptance at the end of the conflict, when the conflict has lost its foothold). Acceptance is therefore not a defeat; it coincides with the conflict and, indeed, with the victory. The oppression of the sickness (which is then no longer oppression) in no way forbids our acceptance of it from the very first. This is true in the same way that war does not, alas, hinder us from esteeming and loving the men whom we exterminate and who exterminate us. But this is a lame comparison, for sickness is not an adversary: it is myself, in a poor posture. On the other hand, the comparison is somewhat apt, for must not my adversary in war also be identical with me in one sole body of woes, that of our humanity?

The body-object of the conflict should in no wise be contrasted or placed before the body-subject of acceptance and reconciliation, the latter following on the failure of the former. These two ways of viewing the world, these two holds on sickness, must coexist and be sustained in a synthesis of life which no longer understands them in a dichotomous fashion. The body-object of the conflict is reunited with the body-subject of integration, to the point of coinciding with it. It is thus that our body becomes the visible place (through our concrete behavior) and the invisible place (through its hidden meaning, which God alone can ascertain) of our choice, in sickness even better than in health; of our choice, not supreme but pathognomic, in the face of death.

II

The preceding is what our patients have to understand, and what we must bring them to understand, through our attitudes as well as our words. We must make them understand that the best way to combat and conquer is neither to flee nor to withdraw into a hostile posture of resentment. There are some people who die of defiance and some who die of hate. Violence has never been the mark of strength. True strength knows how to accept and respect " the other " (the difficulty, the adversary, the event). And true strength, in turn, grows from this respect. I have always remembered this statement of C. G. Jung: "One changes nothing unless one first accepts it."

"One must say *yes* to growing old, to sickness, and let go that which is destined to disappear. Maturity is possible only to the man who abandons the Completed, who listens to his most intimate being and, in constant process of transformation, becomes One with a more profound Being" (Graf von Dürckheim). Such a communion with being should not be confused with a somewhat deist or pantheist quietism. And the "abandoning" involved has nothing in common with the "policy of abandonment" that is the nightmare of the activists. The synthesis of acceptance and of conflict is active and remains personal, face-to-face with the God of revelation.

But it is useful to emphasize, with examples, that activism is not activity, in sickness as well as in politics. We see illnesses arising from the anxious and frenzied resistance to illness. For example, certain resistances to pain accentuate the pain through the muscular contraction which they foster.[134] Several responses are necessary to overcome this problem. For one thing, the patient should be made aware of this abnormal crispation in attitude, respiration, the carriage of the head, the grip of the hand, the seated position, and walking. He should be shown this tension and aggression. He should be made to lower his tensed shoulders and to increase his too superficial costal respiration. The center of gravity of his body should be put where it belongs. In short, we must put this patient in the "correct" attitude and teach him to "stay there" so that, finally, the controlled sickness will leave with the crispation itself and with that awkward resistance that engenders the very fear of sickness.

Our experience furnishes several species of harmful behavior regarding sickness: carelessness and indulgence, instability, short-lived distractions, servility and exploitation in a position of inferiority, all alternate with the violent resentment that I previously described. Crispation and defection become accomplices, the latter defeating and invalidating the great disturbance brought by the former. A patient, forty years of age, has an ulcerous stomach. Many consultations and X-rays are necessary. Hasty actions and contradictory initiative are taken. He is led to spend a fortune in order to be healed; the greatest medical authorities are necessary for him. His stomach must be removed. He will go to any extreme in order to be rid of this ulcer which obsesses him. Yet he will not take care of himself even by getting a little rest or by smoking a few less cigarettes! It reminds one of Sartre's concept of "bad faith." "I can persist in manifesting myself in a certain kind of employment *because* I am inferior in it. . . . It is this fruitless effort which I have chosen, simply because it is fruitless. . . . It is obvious, however, that I can *choose* as a field of action the province in which I am inferior only if this choice implies the reflective *will* to be superior there. To choose to be an inferior artist is of necessity to *wish* to be a great artist." [135] We recognize here patterns of failure behavior, which explain the appearance and persistence of so many pathological functional states.

The best form of combat is that of accepting the rules of the game and the basic givens of the problem, in short, fair play. Our psychotherapy and our pedagogy of the patient force him to bring himself up to the level of his illness, in some way to be the equal of his illness, like a part of a team. We all know that it is the relaxed athlete who wins. The acceptance of sickness in the very midst of competition is no different from the relaxing of the athlete intent on gaining the best "form," the best assets.

But this relaxing is even more, requiring other resources and a different type of grace, in sickness and misfortune. More than a victorious posture, it signifies that I receive what I give. It means that I receive what I give to God and that I belong to him.

There is an aspect that we call "hygienic" in the fair play of the patient, as there is in prayer itself (which Carrel prescribes for our well-being). But there is also an aspect that cannot be reduced to the more or less perfect state or condition of the sick person, namely, that it is a grace received. More correctly, these two aspects are really two readings of one and the same *grace* of the sick person. In one of his books devoted to the First World War, Georges Duhamel mentions the wounded soldiers who "have grace" and others who do not have it, that is, who do not know how to suffer as one should. The word "grace," with its double meaning, shows the two components (aesthetic and religious) of our attitude in illness: grace is both that which I receive and the manner itself in which I react, without stiffness and with adaptability (not "in strength," but with "suppleness").

What is needed is to let oneself go and to let things "go their way." How many times have we tried to bring our patients to a realization that their liver attack, their migraine headache, or whatever, is due to their not having accepted their life, the onslaughts of their daily problems, their marriage, their cramped living space, their neighbors, the insufficiency of their salary even when it is augmented by a second job, their lack of children, or the fear of having children. It requires that they become aware of their total situation and of accepting it or accommodating themselves to it (but in the sense that the eye accommodates itself to distance, or the legs to the length of the jump). It is a matter of adapting an attitude to a situation, of adopting the correct attitude (neither a tone that is too high — falsetto — nor one too low).

Our methods of communicating the *correct* attitude to our patients must go beyond the elementary techniques of presence and of counsel, and beyond the customary techniques of the explicative and comprehensive word. These methods must engage us with the patients in a relationship of therapeutic reciprocity where the whole man, with his own psychological and psychoanalytic implications and with his personal religious resources, puts himself body and soul in the service of the other and is ready to exchange with the other his experience on all levels.[136]

III

The body is the locus of our choice. This is the first and last word of our study, and this is why I wrote to Paul Tournier, when he announced the theme of the 1960 Medicine of the Person conference: " The body is paradoxically and at one and the same time the locus of individuation and particularism, on the one hand, and the locus of interchange and love, on the other hand." It would have been artificial to make these two " parts " of the same study, for they are two indissociable poles of the same option.

The body is the language that God has given to us in order to know him or to ignore him, to understand him or to reject him, to cooperate or to refuse to cooperate in the creation. And the body is also the means God uses to make all this known to us. It is the language from him to us and from us to him. This is why we have dared to say that the body is given to us as a sacrament.

As physicians, then, we must show love for the body. This is not the exclusive and limited attention of the scientist, for whom the body does not exist beyond its visible boundaries, but rather, the attention that one devotes to a message, to a code, the code of our deepest problems, and even more profoundly, the code of our incarnation.

My body is the enigmatic code of my temporality in my eternity.

I indicated previously a parallel with the question of sex, and the parallelism holds true in this respect. We must accord to sex neither a mystical-romantic idolatry nor an idealistic contempt (which comes to the same thing). Rather, we must give to sex a respect that locates it in love and in the axis of the entire creation.

Yes, the body must be *situated.* This protects us, as physicians, from a pseudospiritualistic mysticism fond of vague theories and ignoring exact dosages, for it makes us treat the body-subject *without ignoring* the body-object of our patients (under pain of major errors).

Technical dualism is an indispensable part of our profession and must be preserved. This cannot be repeated enough. I think that I have emphasized it sufficiently in this study, which otherwise could easily lead to confusion. The danger confronting physicians of the person would be that of a predualist woolliness of thinking, I would even say, of a certain prepersonalist infantilism, which is as far as possible from a true adult personalism. Our objective, in reality, is to progress toward a *postdualism,* beyond dualism (which is not the same as ignoring it).

Far from ignoring the techniques, we must, of course, utilize them in order to go beyond them; but we will have the right to go beyond the body-object only when we have granted it its own. The objective and technical *moment* of the body must be integrated into the Medicine of the Person. The subtle and simple meaning of the incommunicable intimity and the indivisible totality of the person-subject is so often lacking in our physician-technicians. However, when we have acquired or rediscovered this meaning, we must not fall into the opposite error, namely, of becoming hostile and impermeable to the physicochemical aspect of the body.

Certainly, the *outside* inevitably masks the *inside* of man, to the degree that, considering the *inside* itself, one turns it into an *outside* despite oneself.[137] But we should guard against the contrary, that is, that through our increasing concern with the *inside* we become incapable of being of help to the outside and of being able to make use of the outside. To become thus insensitive to man's external nature would be to imperil both ourselves and our patients.[138]

We must grasp the totality of the two aspects of life, which is an *inner-outer* thing (which is true of the universe, if one accepts the insights of Teilhard de Chardin, for example); each one continues to appeal to the other, to serve somehow as the indicative of the other. This is not at all a verbal conciliation of irreconcilables, nor of those syntheses which are possible only with the result of clear-obscurity and troubled water. Rather, it involves the very synthesis of life and our incarnation itself. The subjective and the objective approaches interpenetrate each other to the point where each one cooperates with the other through the interplay of contrasts and indices.[139]

There is a " visible " body, that of the surgeon and of the behavioral psychosociologist. And there is the " invisible " body, the meaningful body, that of the perspective of the physician of the person, who, in effect, accommodates his perspective to the same wavelength of the philosopher and the believer. It is not distance, but proximity. Now, the invisible must not hide the visible, no more than the visible should mask the meaning of which it is the sign.

The body is body, and *more* than body. The body overflows the body; it is *more* than it is itself. It is charged with a meaning that makes of it a sign and a sacrament.

Thus we will never forget that the techniques applied to the body-object also involve the body-subject which we do not " see." That is, they involve the totality of the person, which we see and do not see. And it is the completeness and the flowering of the whole man that remains the project of the physician, whether he removes part of the stomach or prescribes some type of ointment.

IV

In Chapter IV, I pointed out what is meant by the movement of transcendence and by the meaning of transcendence. Neither one must separate us from our corporeality and from our incarnation. Our body is the very code of our own transcendence and the code of God's transcendence itself.[140] A movement of transcendence that would quite rightly restore the infinite distance of God without however incarnating it in our most material and most mundane life (that of our body and of our relationships with men), would be an evasion in the smoke of an idealism that furnishes the most fallacious substitute for transcendence, its hollow and void form. Transcendence is full and heavy with immediate reality.

The incarnating movement does not succeed the movement of transcendence as though to counterbalance or compensate for it and to set its feet firmly on the ground. No, the movement of transcendence is authentic and proves itself only if it *is* incarnating. Otherwise, and we repeat, it is false transcendence, a type of abstract vertical takeoff, a satellite operation suppressing gravity without changing perspective. The movement of transcendence is in no way contrary to gravity, as certain religious images (e.g., a poor understanding of the ascension) would give us to believe. It bears no resemblance to a vertical takeoff which, whatever be the power of the airplane, would never produce anything but a change of power, not a change of order.

It is said, in a manner of speaking, that the movement of incarnation "returns" to the body in order to "restore" its truth to it. There, indeed, is where we will find true transcendence, contained in the meaning that will invest our body, as members of the body of Christ, the universal body, that is, associated in the plan of God. It is not in an *elsewhere* or a *beyond* of the body that transcendence resides; it is in the body itself, as sign.

The personalist ambition is a delicate undertaking and one doomed to many misapprehensions. We have pointed out at least two such misapprehensions. First of all, we are waylaid by the sentimental and subjectivist woolliness. But there is also this type of compromise or balancing, of verbal synthesis between the movement of transcendence and the "return" to earth of our corporeality, of our incarnation. The one offsets the other. Now, transcendence in the midst of incarnation is neither a synthesis nor a compromise. Rather, it is an experience, or, properly speaking, the mystical experience.

It is not to be a mystic, nor to formulate mystical doctrine. (But what do we know of the confines of the active and mundane mysticism that we skirt? And would not we be wrong to imagine that mysticism is reserved to the " specialists," to a few exceptional souls?) However, it is to work in the same vein, or in the same furrow, namely, of respecting the body and of creating respect for the body in our patients.

To respect my sick body, or the bodies of my patients, is not to reveal me as either materialist or spiritualist. It is quite simply to reintegrate the body in his house, the house of the Spirit. It is to reintegrate the body in transcendence, which does not reign supreme elsewhere, but is sheltered in its own bosom.

This is undoubtedly the true meaning of Personalism. The person unites the singular with the universal, the individual body with the body of Christ. It is these two bodies (but one would be wrong to suppose that they can be added together) that constitute really the person. These " two bodies " *are one and the same body invested with two meanings, one of which retrieves and takes in charge the other.* Christ, in the same way, takes humanity in charge in order to raise it to him. This is why Christianity speaks less willingly of the immortality of the soul than of the resurrection of men. In this way it gives witness to the transcendence of the incarnation and to the spiritual significance of the visible body.

Who, then, more than physicians, devoted to the health of the body, could understand, teach, and practice the infinite dignity of our work, if it is true that the medicine of the body and the medicine of the soul are abstractions, and that there is only one single medicine, aiming at one single health and one single blessedness, the medicine of the body-spirit, *the Medicine of the Person.*

NOTES

Introduction

1. This book continues and develops the report given in August, 1960, at the Thirteenth International Week of the Medicine of the Person. In the midst of a work community, such as that of Bossey (World Council of Churches conference center near Geneva — TRANSLATOR), precise details concerning goals and methods are understood. But when addressed to a larger medical and nonmedical public, it becomes essential to state ends and methods. Our study would lack effectiveness were we not to give a comprehensible account of its language and its method.

2. Paul Ricoeur, *Finitude et culpabilité* (Paris: Aubier, 1960), Vol. II, p. 324.

3. *Ibid.*, p. 332.

4. Jacques Sarano, *La Guérison* (Paris: Presses Universitaires de France, 1955), p. 21.

5. "Among the majority of men, non-belief in one thing is based on the blind belief in another thing." (Lichtemberger, quoted in Ed. Morin, *Autocritique*, Julliard, 1960.)

6. Numerous examples could be given. My style of life is expressed and betrayed by the way in which I receive, listen to, interrupt, examine, and handle a patient. Yet it is even more glaringly expressed in my diagnosis and its formulation, in the choice that I pose and that I impose of a surgical mutilation. Everywhere and always my person as physician and as the man that I am, with or without religious choices, orients me and orients the lives and futures of my patients. This is hidden behind the pseudo-objectivity

of the technique ("That should not be said," and we pretend that it does not exist).

7. I have had to point out elsewhere that certain tendencies tend to make a *specialty* of psychosomatic medicine and that our present-day medical practice will come more and more into conflict with this idea. "Psychosomatic" patients are becoming increasingly prevalent in the clientele of the general practitioner (with a corresponding decrease in the number of patients with purely organic difficulties). This type of patient will become either a limit or a conventional rule. The general practitioner (taking into account his personal aptitudes and the education he has received) will be a psychosomaticist whether he likes it or not, or else he will cease to be. In the same way, the psychosomaticist will be a general practitioner, or else he will be in danger of falling into an objective technique (the trap of all specialties as such, including psychiatry).

8. As we will see later, there is a problem of the soul-object, which is even more acute than that of the body-object.

9. Cf., for example, *Médecine et médecins* (Paris: Seuil, 1959), etc.

10. Cf. Ch. I, section III, and Practical Conclusion, section III.

11. The idea of *totality* can be made more precise through a consideration of its two meanings. The totality of objective *comprehension* is based on the cohesion and the coherence of the world of objects ("the machine of the planets is necessary for the simple flight of the butterfly"). The sciences progress toward Science, because through their specialties they aim at understanding the *whole*, of which their particular objects are a part.

The totality of *option* is located on the level of freedom. Man, in order to be man, seeks not only to understand the world but to *make* it, to create it. The global project of making the human world is based on an option that bears on the *whole*, that orients the entire life and gives it meaning. Medicine is concerned with this double plan of the totality of objective comprehension (as science) and of the totality of option and of realization (as therapeutic "praxis"). It is both medicine of the object (to understand) and medicine of the subject (to create).

12. Marxism, as a total option, and *a*theism seem to me to be of the same genre as the religious option (in the most general sense, of course, since they designate those who witness to *ir*religion). What I mean is that this option goes beyond (transcends) the man who *dedicates* himself to his cause, and it goes beyond much of that which he says of it himself (our temptation being rightly to grant him *more* than he intends to admit).

13. Cf. Michael Balint, *The Doctor, His Patient and the Illness* (London: Pitman Medical Publishing Company, Ltd., and New York: International Universities Press, Inc., 1957).

PART ONE

Chapter I

14. Jean-Paul Sartre, *Being and Nothingness* (Philosophical Library, Inc., 1956), p. 329.

15. Translator's Note: Paul Ricoeur utilizes the word *dicibilité* to express the nature of something that permits it to be spoken of in a clear and precise manner, as opposed to *indicibilité*, which is similar to the English word "ineffability."

16. This is the inverse parallel of that which, in 1950, I outlined in an essay on evil. The reencounter is curious. Here is the passage: "Ethics expresses man's effort to adapt himself to the inexplicable existence of evil in this world. One cannot try to understand one without the other. Having frankly faced evil as such, we must then ask ourselves what will be our ethical response. The one should act on the other as the vaccine on the bacillus, the antibody on the antigen, etc."

17. Cf. *La Guérison*, pp. 11 ff.; *Études philosophiques*, No. 4, 1955, pp. 726 ff.

18. At the same time, this life and this physionomy of the amputated fragment make it something other than an object and initiate the individuality-subject of the living body, which we will consider later. The two aspects interpenetrate. The fragment of worm is *object*, which the remaining body replaces; or *subject*, which reconstitutes the rest of the body.

19. Cf. *La Guérison*, Ch. II, and *Esprit*, No. 2, 1957, pp. 272 ff.

20. It is necessary not to evade technical progress, but to integrate it, and the temptation of Lanza del Vastro's ark does not seem to me to be valid (Lanza del Vasto is the leader of a French ascetic, antimodern group which has rejected the amenities of modern society.—Translator.)

21. Cf. "Pluralité des voies d'accès thérapeutiques," *Présences*, Revue du monde des malades, No. 81, 1962. This same review published elements of this present essay on the body in its issue No. 74, 1961.

22. Certain considerations on the wearying excesses of the tension of organic defense inspire techniques called "artificial hibernation."

23. Listen to Zarathustra: "Once the soul looked contemptu-

ously on the body, and then that contempt was the supreme thing — the soul wished the body meager, ghastly, and famished. Thus it thought to escape from the body and the earth. Oh, that soul was itself meager, ghastly, and famished; and cruelty was the delight of that soul! But ye, also, my brethren, tell me: What doth your body say about your soul?" *The Philosophy of Nietzsche* (Modern Library, Inc., n.d.), p. 7.

CHAPTER II

24. I do not intend to develop here a theory of normality and of pathology, but the remainder of my analysis will show the positive and structural aspect of anomaly. Cf. *La Guérison*, Ch. I, and Fr. Duyckaerts, *La Notion de normal en psychologie clinique* (Vrin, 1954). Cf. also *Présences*, No. 77, 4th quarter 1961.

25. Ricoeur, *Finitude et culpabilité*, p. 104.

26. Cf. the whole psychology of *attitudes*, for example, in *Symp. de l'Association de psychologie de langue française*, Bordeaux, 1959 (Paris: Presses Universitaires de France, 1961), pp. 88 ff.

27. Perhaps it will seem strange to make the body assume responsibility for neuroses, of which psychoanalysis has correctly shown the psychological origin, contrary to psychosomatic and somatic illnesses where psychogenesis and organogenesis intervene together. Is this not to confuse the unconscious and the somatic? I want to say simply that the attitude adopted by an illness is always mixed, with a decisive participation of the body, even in neuroses (i.e., illnesses of psychological and situational origin). And this will not be *due* to the role of the unconscious, but, if I may say so, *despite* the psychic nature of this unconscious and the psychogenesis of neurosis. Not only hysteria, but all neuroses are postures strongly involving corporeal participation, which social and verbal attitudes deny before the public.

28. Balint, *op. cit.*

29. The twenty hours of psychology provided for in the new programs of the medical faculties in France only have merit in denouncing the previous absence of such formation; twenty hours cannot hope to fill the void. A seminar on the model of Balint's London seminar (*op. cit.*) has recently been started in Paris. Let us also note certain promising attempts throughout France (*Concours médical*, No. 49, 1961, pp. 6299 ff.).

30. TRANSLATOR'S NOTE: It will perhaps be noted that throughout the book "the patient" habitually complains of liver ailments. This hardy and efficient organ is thought by the Frenchman to be the locus or cause of all his ailments, so that, in the words of Dr.

André Varay, an eminent French liver specialist, "French liver trouble is almost a chauvinistic attribute" (*Time*, December 27, 1963). The French even treat their household pets for liver attacks.

31. Cf. *La Guérison*, p. 16.

32. *Ibid.*, p. 53.

33. For this critique, cf. *Médecine et médecins* and articles in *Esprit*, No. 10, 1960; No. 5, 1962.

34. TRANSLATOR'S NOTE: The French social security system includes a program of socialized medicine.

35. Social security also assumes the expenses of psychic illnesses, to be sure. But this is still the *soul-object*, not the subject, which occupies the psychiatrist ordinarily.

36. Cf. *Médecine et médecins*, pp. 201 ff.

37. Let us add to this the prodigious proliferation of drugs coming out of innumerable laboratories, calling into play publicity whose excesses border on the absurd. The effect of these publicity campaigns is to cancel out each other through a type of game similar to radio-jamming, producing general obscurity. Mistrust also results, for the most innocuous piece of technical information is suspected of serving commercial interests. The salesmen besiege us and shamelessly suggest: "Your patients *demand* that you change your medicines." I cite a prospectus that I have under my eyes (if only I could reproduce the pictures!):

"*Change . . . Again change . . . Always change!*"

"The world," a humorist has said, "is a hospital where each patient is possessed with the desire to switch beds! . . . This desire to change is verified in all areas. It is found in your waiting room, where all of your gastro-hepatic patients await from you the 'new remedy,' 'the latest fashion in therapeutics.' You can easily satisfy these demands by prescribing. . . ."

Everyone knows that medicines are made not to assure health, but to satisfy the demands of the patients!

38. Balint (*op. cit.*) is harsh regarding reassuring and sterile reports of specialists, including those of the psychiatrist (whom he does not spare, being one himself). The specialist, in his eyes, could have only the place of an occasional auxiliary expert to be consulted by the general practitioner, who is alone in knowing the man and in taking responsibility for his life. This solution cuts medicine in two: the specialist would be poorly resigned to the role to which he is destined, that of a devoted servant, fallen from the royal throne which he usurps today. Certain specialists, of whom I am one, have not abandoned the ambition of examining man through their neurologic, cardiac, or digestive approaches. It is quite a

drama to see how they defend themselves against the armor into which one wants to put them, *the segregation of the specialist!* It is true that others dream of nothing better than such a role of expert without responsibility. Only a collegial system of medicine can permit them not to lose the man in them, that is, the physician.

39. *Esprit,* February 1957.

CHAPTER III

40. *Journal métaphysique,* especially pp. 236 ff.; *Du Refus à l'invocation* (Gallimard, 1940), pp. 27 ff.

41. So also with naturalistic explications of sexuality, whose artificial objectivity does not do justice to personal depth (cf. J. Sarano, "L'esprit, le sexe et la bête," *Esprit,* No. XI, 1960, p. 1852).

42. To give a trite example, does not the forgetting of an appointment morally engage a man, who, by this same forgetting, unveils who he is?

43. This is one of the defects of Marxist praxis, which sometimes makes all dialogue impossible. The practical and dialectical mixing of the statement of fact and the exigence leads to the placing of "bad faith" throughout. We should also call attention here to a regrettable relationship between a certain "dogmatism of perspicacity" (Belaval) of the "depth" psychologists and certain reductions of Marxist criticism.

44. I am alluding to a valuable distinction on which P. Ricoeur has insisted (cf., for example, his article in *Esprit,* Nos. 8 and 9, 1954).

45. On the progress of the attitude of comprehension in relation to the attitude of accusation, cf. my study *La Culpabilité* (Paris: Colin, 1957), Ch. 2.

46. Cf. especially G. Marcel, *op. cit.;* Sartre, *Being and Nothingness,* pp. 365 ff.; Merleau-Ponty (cited farther on); Emmanuel Mounier, *Traité du caractère,* pp. 117 ff.; *La Personnalisme* (Paris: Presses Universitaires de France, 1950), Ch. 1; etc.

47. TRANSLATOR'S NOTE: The term "body image" is taken from the English translation of Merleau-Ponty's *Phenomenology of Perception.* The French term (*schéma corporel*) would be literally translated as the "diagram" or "scheme" of the body.

48. Merleau-Ponty, *Phénoménologie de la Perception* (9th ed.; Paris: Gallimard, 1945), Part I, pp. 81–235.

49. *Ibid.,* pp. 103–104, 143.

50. J. Wahl defines the body as the "essential habit that conditions all the others," *Traité de métaphysique* (Paris: Payot, 1957), p. 365.

51. Merleau-Ponty, *op. cit.*, p. 110.

52. Kurt Goldstein, *La Structure de l'organisme,* French translation (Paris: Gallimard, 1951), pp. 177 ff.

53. *Ibid.*, p. 179.

54. Experiments on animals (Goldstein, *op. cit.*, pp. 180–181) show that a disorder produces variants of this same movement of normalization: a frog immediately utilizes a different leg to rub if one amputates the leg it habitually uses to remove a drop of acid on its back.

55. Merleau-Ponty, *op. cit.*, p. 134.

56. *Ibid.*, pp. 132, 136.

57. I have been surprised at the unjustified and misguided criticism directed by Medard Boss, *Introduction à la médecine psychosomatique,* French translation (Paris: Presses Universitaires de France, 1959), a devotee of the Heideggerian philosophy of *Dasein,* against the works on the body of the French existentialists, G. Marcel, Merleau-Ponty, Sartre, Ricoeur, *et al.* " These authors too often no sooner formulate their existential theses than they contradict them " (p. 46).

It seems to me that such a procedure stops at the letter of a language that, inevitably and despite the authors, falls back into objectification (including the language of *Dasein*). It is a partial criticism that picks out certain formulas without paying attention to their contexts. These contexts precisely point out the insufficiency of the formulas and try to suggest the idea of the body-subject beyond them. " Especially in G. Marcel, the body is seen to be a simple instrument " (p. 47). The constant and direct evidence of Marcel's work gives no basis for such a statement.

The other difficulty concerns a fundamental problem, not simply a problem of language. This fundamental problem is that in our meaning the body lends itself, at one and the same time, to the two perspectives of the object and the subject. " It is inadmissible," writes Boss, " that so many modern anthropologists (like Plessner, Sartre, Marcel, Merleau-Ponty) say, in one and the same phrase, that man *has* a body and that he is his body. Indeed, in order to take seriously these two parts of the phrase, it would be necessary to reconcile two perspectives (and this is impossible): that of an ' instrumental' conception that sees only utilizable objects, and that of being, revealing human nature in an existential sense " (p. 35). I think that Boss wants to prove too much. . . . If the body were not *in a certain manner an object*, would we even have to bother contesting Boss? Agreed, this is a " superstition " or a convention, and I am in full accord with Boss's thesis, but we cannot be content with mocking this superstition or convention; we must take account of it and draw out its meaning. Descartes was right against Descartes and against his too hasty detractors when he said, concerning the soul and the body, that " it is necessary to think of them as one sole thing and together to think of them as two, in contrast " (" thing " should not be taken literally). I do not know that the perspective of *Dasein* has overcome this mystery of our incarnation, which makes both my body-object and my body-subject true.

58. In the course of a learned philosophical debate, a listener exclaimed: " Can you give me a definition of God! " There was general amazement, for this was completely off the subject. In truth, had someone given in to this request and attempted to give a definition of God, it would have been certain that it was not God of whom they were speaking. If God is, he is precisely beyond definition.

59. G. Madinier, *Conscience et signification* (Paris: Presses Universitaires de France, 1953), p. 4.

60. *Ibid.*, p. 6.

61. In this sense, the snare of the *soul-object* is analogous to the snare of the *body-object*.

62. Some interesting perspectives will be found in Victor Poucel's *Plaidoyer pour le corps* (Le Puy: éditions Xavier Mappus), although there is also present an excessive apologetic enthusiasm from which one may or may not profit. Consider the miracle of the erect posture (pp. 25 ff.): " What! this so delicate heavy mass, whose joints are ready to bend all at once, and you will balance yourself on these slender bases! . . . A pure mathematical mind could not envisage the standing man: what calculations would ever lead his mind to suspicion such a thing? . . . Every man, in standing up, defies pure matter, and the ease of his posture is in itself a victorious homage to the spirit whose delight marks it."

63. I am not speaking here of the diagnosis of death itself, of which current methods of resuscitation have multiplied the difficulties and have literally rocked the bases.

64. The sickness-as-refuge, the " conducts of bodily responsibility " of Hesnard, the resistances to healing and " sicknesses of healing " (*La Guérison*, p. 103) are so many proofs of the unity of the sick body-subject, tightened into a special conduct called sickness.

65. Merleau-Ponty, *op. cit.*

66. *La Guérison*, pp. 116 ff.

67. Cf. Mounier, *Traité du caractère* (Paris: Seuil, 1947), p. 117.

CHAPTER IV

68. That is, judgment as such, not as it is produced in a given place, at a given time, in a given individual: as event, judgment is obviously part of the world of psychology.

69. Raymond Ruyer, *Néo-finalisme* (Paris: Presses Universitaires de France, 1952).

70. For the spirit at work in the biological world, see (other than Ruyer, *op. cit.*) Pradines, *L'Aventure de l'esprit dans les espèces* (Paris: Flammarion, 1954), for example, pp. 70–71. It goes without saying that to state: " *There is* spirit (an organizing activity) in an embryo or an electron " is not to state that *they are* spirit. Both are the place of an activity which they cannot assign to themselves.

71. J. Lacroix, *Marxisme, Existentialisme, Personnalisme* (Paris: Presses Universitaires de France, 1955), p. 47.

72. Madinier, *op. cit.*, p. 38.

73. " Logische Untersuchungen," quoted in Gaston Berger, *Le Cogito dans la phénoménologie de Husserl* (Paris: Aubier, 1941), p. 24.

74. On this point, cf. Introduction, section VIII.

75. The " ascending " transcendence can, however, designate simply a mundane moving beyond, homogeneous to ourselves, which does not dominate the temporal order (for example, the Marxist moving beyond such as it defines itself).

76. " When is it necessary to be joyful? In danger, over a depth of ten thousand fathoms, miles and miles from all human aid." (Quoted in *Études kierkegaardiennes* by Jean Wahl, Vrin, p. 340.) " That which is higher than despair is to be joyful at the moment where anxiety surrounds us on all sides, out over ten thousand fathoms." (*Ibid.*, p. 109.)

77. On this point, see our article " L'Homme d'aujourd'hui et les sciences anthropologiques," in *Parole et mission, L'Annonce de l'évangile aujourd 'hui* (Paris: Éditions du cerf, 1962).

78. Ruyer, *op. cit.*, p. 2.

79. To the reader who is scandalized by this language, let me refer him once again to the Introduction, section VIII.

80. *La Culpabilité* (Paris: Colin, 1957).

81. *La Culpabilité*, pp. 161–163. The following passage, taken from the same work, concerns our purpose: " The spiritual exigence of man is incarnated. It announces itself and renounces itself; it converts itself as it perverts itself, in the midst of the lived, of the carnal, of the biological. Existential anxiety is an integral part of our spiritual exigence. It could not be considered as an unfor-

tunate weight of matter or of morbidity. No, this anxiety belongs to the very spirituality of my experience. The incarnation of this experience in the midst of lived existence is part of its promotion of existence into the concrete spiritual. It is its own manner of being spiritual: far from adulterating it, such an incarnation adds to it its own measure of carnal generosity." Far from being the prison of the spirit, the body is the sign of it.

PART TWO

82. In the physiognomy, is it the body that defines the soul, or is it content with being its own image? As we will see, this is a false problem, because it rests on a false duality of the body and soul, an Orphic or Platonic abstraction. Let us say that the body is the expression of the soul: one sole reality, for life and for death — and for the resurrection.

83. Cf. *La Guérison*, last chapter, especially p. 115.

84. It has been repeated since Aristotle that nothing is in the mind that has not been in the sense, except the mind itself. By that is meant that the body furnishes the materials that are indispensable to the very functioning of the mind. My intention here is to go farther and recall that, not only the contents, but also the a priori absolutes are movement and body. The mind establishes distinctions, unifications, and *relationships* ("but," "in spite of," "then," etc.) only because it has a body.

CHAPTER V

85. G. Madinier, *Conscience et mouvement* (Paris: Presses Universitaires de France, 1938).

86. *Ibid.*, p. 408.

87. Cf. Bergson, *Matière et mémoire.*

88. "L'Âme et le corps," in *La Pensée et le mouvant* (Paris: Presses Universitaires de France, 1934).

89. *Le Moi, le monde et Dieu*, p. 50, quoted in Madinier, *op. cit.*, p. 412.

90. Madinier, *op. cit.*, p. 413.

91. *Ibid.*, p. 416.

92. *Ibid.*, p. 422.

93. *Les Sens de la défense*, p. 284, quoted in Madinier, *op. cit.*, p. 429.

94. Madinier, *op. cit.*, p. 441.

95. *Ibid.*, p. 440.

96. This is true to such an extent that to speak of a divine "thought" has no meaning other than analogically. All that can be

said is that it is absolutely other and beyond that which we call "thought." We come to a knowledge of God's plans only through the mediation of Christ.

97. Madinier, *op. cit.*, p. 449.

Chapter VI

98. The psychological description is taken up again here as the *sign* of our incarnation.

99. Henri Bouchet, *Introduction à la philosophie de l'individu* (Paris: Flammarion, 1949), p. 125.

100. "It places me in space and places space in me," writes Madinier. "It is the form of all distinguishing: it belongs to movement to distinguish; it is the instrument of dissection and analysis, the constructor of totalities, the maker of schema and, at the same time, it is the principle of opposition." (*Op. cit.*, p. 450.)

101. Here again, it is necessary to view psychological election as the *index* of election in the spiritual sense.

102. "Concealment," writes Paul Ricoeur, "is still an episode of manifestation. . . . The latent meaning could only be an exegesis of the apparent meaning, as the search for a better meaning: Nonsense or senselessness is still in the dimension of sense. . . . As far as one can and should go in being suspicious of the apparent meaning, it is the apparent meaning that introduces the impetus in the dimensions of the meaning. . . . And psychotherapeutics, in proceeding to this exegesis of meaning, want only to bring about the acceptance of a new sense that would be lived on a more authentic level." (*Finitude et culpabilité*, Vol. I, p. 104.)

103. Translator's Note: Antaeus, a giant of Libya, compelled passing strangers to wrestle with him. When thrown, he received fresh strength from contact with his mother earth (Ge).

104. Among the personalist philosophers, Emmanuel Mounier was the most influential thinker. In his works and in the review *Esprit,* which he founded in 1932, he studied the problem that occupies us most especially in *Le Personnalisme* (Paris: Presses Universitaires de France, 1949), and *Traité du caractère* (Paris: Seuil, 1947).

105. Bergson's language is no longer completely our own, in this quotation as in others.

106. Bergson, *The Two Sources of Morality and Religion* (Henry Holt & Company, Inc., 1935), pp. 246, 247.

Chapter VII

107. To say " it " regarding my body already betrays my thought and sacrifices once more to dualist language, against which it is necessary to guard constantly.

108. TRANSLATOR'S NOTE: Alexey Kirillov, in Dostoevsky's *The Possessed*, is a revolutionary obsessed with the desire to commit suicide, thereby asserting his freedom of will.

109. The same contempt is sometimes held regarding God. Believers who, with the best intentions, reduced God to some disembodied ideal or some idol, are no different from the atheists who (with some reason) reject this idol or this ideal. Atheism and deism, under opposite appearances, have missed the true face of the living God.

110. " Nothing is more materialistic than to scorn a pleasure because it is purely material " (Chesterton).

111. Mounier, *Traité du caractère*, p. 121n.

112. I refer to my article " L'Esprit, le sexe et la bête," *Esprit*, special number on sexuality, November, 1960.

113. As will have been observed, I do not intend, in this book, to enter into the doctrinal distinction between the body-soul dualism and the body-soul-spirit " trialism." A summary dualism locates the dividing line between the body and the soul. The only acceptable philosophical dualism distinguishes the body-soul from the spirit, the biopsychological from the spiritual (or the logical, or the transcendental). Cf. Ch. IV.

114. " The idea of *necessity* appears second, like the fruit of an abstraction or a revolt: it is the extract of the experience of communion through fault, through seism, division, through which slips the nothingness of the ' for self ' (*pour-soi*), the autopositioning of the ' small I,' the analytical and separatist understanding. ' Necessity ' is born of my intention to evade myself, to disobey: it determines that to which I will give only grudging obedience. The intention of evading has the name *necessity*. It is a lost unity, which only a long search can rediscover: the unity of necessity and liberty is not ' of this world ' " (*Esprit*, p. 1862). Analogous reflections on *evil* can be found in *La Douleur*, Vol. I, Part II.

115. TRANSLATOR'S NOTE: The term is from Gayraud Wilmore's *The Secular Relevance of the Church* (The Westminster Press, 1962), *passim*.

116. Again, it is necessary to interpret this idealistic deviation of Christianity in its historical and spiritual context. The renunciation of the world in no way hinders one from giving his life. This

renunciation simply determines the spirit in which I consecrate my activity in the world without egoistically loving myself in it. Thus it does not turn me away from the world, but, on the contrary, decenters me in it, which is the best way to serve the world. Renunciation of the world is not necessarily escape from the world.

117. We cannot here elaborate on the mystery of the harmony and the discordances between "saintliness" and "health" (cf. "Les trois dimensions ou promotions de la santé," in *Présences*, No. 77, 1961).

118. Bergson, *L'Énergie spirituelle.*

CHAPTER VIII

119. Marcel, "La Maladie comme mystère crucial," in *Présences*, No. 51, 1955, p. 13.

120. We will see later the qualifications and the conditions that can accompany this language. In the same way, the terms "resignation," "merit," etc., do not have a narrowly ethical meaning, but cover a wider anthropological area.

121. In her report to the Thirteenth International Week of the Medicine of the Person, Bossey, August, 1960 (published in *Présences*, No. 74, 1961).

122. "La Double Tentation," special number on medicine, *Esprit*, February, 1957, pp. 274–275.

123. Cf. my article "Les Trois Dimensions de la santé," *Présences*, No. 77, 1961, p. 14.

124. TRANSLATOR'S NOTE: Semeiology is the science dealing with the use of signs (in medicine, symptomatology).

125. "Peccancy" is not in our vocabulary; sin and fault do not come under the perspective of the physician. The word "pride," for example, does not have the same sound in the physician's office and in the confessional.

126. We must guard against a picturesque language, such as: "One has the sickness, the body, the government that one deserves," and not mean it in the strict sense of a punishment. Yet it must be acknowledged, in referring back to my commentary on G. Marcel, that modern man is more conscious of the interpenetration of the two languages of statement and exigence.

127. During the Thirteenth International Week of the Medicine of the Person.

128. Cf. Gesel, *L'Embryologie du comportement* (Paris: Presses Universitaires de France, 1953).

129. Porak, quoted by Robert, *op. cit.*

130. This, of course, in a wider sense of the narrow theological meaning of the religious sacraments properly so-called, which number seven.

PRACTICAL CONCLUSION

131. Cf. *Médecine et médecins,* especially p. 228: " It is a general rule in man that he who is not *more* than he is, betrays what he is. . . . The physician obeys this rule, which obligates him to do *more* than prescribe his own technical or statistical definition. This *more* belongs to the strict necessity of his definition in its very exactness. This surplus is the necessary minimum. If he is not *more* than physician, he is less than physician."

132. Cf. *La Douleur* (Paris: Éditions de l'Épi, 1965). Extracts from this work have appeared in *Les Études philosophiques,* No. 4, 1959: " La Douleur, deux fonctions pour un échec"; and in *Présences,* No. I, 1960: " A quoi sert la douleur."

133. Sartre, *The Flies,* Act II, Scene II.

134. We know of many examples of pain fostered and exacerbated by muscular contraction that it has begun in the first place. It is a vicious physiopathological circle (cf. *La Guérison,* Ch. I).

135. Sartre, *Being and Nothingness,* p. 472.

136. On the relations of psychoanalysis, which represents a particular technique highly specialized, and the therapeutic relationship such as we have outlined here in the spirit of the Medicine of the Person, let us say simply that the medicine of the person must be acquainted with psychoanalysis and utilize it according to the perspectives that have been tested by Balint in his training center (*op. cit*), and that the Medicine of the Person must go farther.

137. This is the problem of the *soul-object,* the snare of all psychotherapeutic techniques.

138. Cf. *Médecine et médecins,* where I insist on the necessity of the objective moment. It is an interplay of objectivity and intersubjectivity. He who leans too far toward one side must preach the other, and take a good look at the alternative.

139. We have seen (Ch. III) how the discovery of the body-subject can come to us through ways as different as the reflections of a Gabriel Marcel and the structural analyses of a Merleau-Ponty.

140. Much can be learned from the great mystics, who have approached the heights of the mystery of infinite distance, yet who have come to the point of seeing with the eyes and touching with the hands this presence of transcendence. See, for example, Georges Morel, *Le Sens de l'existence selon St-Jean de la Croix* (Paris: Aubier, 1960). Saint John of the Cross speaks of " spiritual visions of

heavenly material realities " (quoted in Vol. II, p. 102), " spiritual corporeal substances," which, according to Morel, are seen and even *touched*. " The mystic, like the majority of mystics, speaks of the *touches* of God: ' *Los toques de Dios*.' " (P. 124.)